From Apollo to Artemis:

Stories From My 50 Years With NASA

Herb Baker

Herb Baker

First Edition

This is a work of nonfiction. All people, events, locations, and situations are portrayed to the best of the author's memory.

ISBN: 979-8-218-45902-4 (paperback)

Cover design by: Julie Adams

Printed in the United States of America

This book is dedicated to my wife, Karen, and my sons, Brandon and Andrew

Table of Contents

Introduction

If you've ever wondered what it was like to work at NASA from the days of Apollo through the Shuttle and Space Station Programs, all the way to the beginnings of the Artemis Program, you might enjoy this book.

My first job on-site at NASA was in 1969, as a teenager, working with the news media covering the Apollo 11 mission. I continued that temporary work intermittently with TV networks for about five years, covering several other NASA missions. I then had a 42-year career with NASA and have been an officer on the NASA Alumni League-Johnson Space Center Board of Directors for four years. Altogether, I've been involved with NASA for a little over 50 years.

I am not an astronaut, engineer, or scientist. I worked with and became friends with many people in those professions over the years, but most of my NASA career was spent in the business/procurement office as a contracting officer and office manager. You will find some, but not a lot of, technical discussions about spaceflight and spacecraft in this book. This book is more focused on people and events, and what it's like to work at NASA, than trying to explain orbital mechanics or how a rocket engine works.

Having been lucky enough to have a long career at NASA, I've had the privilege of being involved in many interesting activities and meeting many fascinating people. I retired from NASA in 2017 and, since that time, as I've shared these experiences, many of my friends have told me that I should write a book. Shortly after retiring, I wrote the foreword for a science fiction novel titled *Earth Escape*, written by my friend Réal Laplaine, but that's entirely different from writing a book.

I've never had a desire to become an author nor am I looking for any recognition that might come from publishing a book. However, I've often been reminded that my family might appreciate having some of these stories written down, so I never completely dismissed the idea.

There have been hundreds of books written about NASA and space exploration, many of them by astronauts and other NASA legends, such as Chris Kraft (*Flight*), Gene Kranz (*Failure Is Not an Option*), Glynn Lunney (*Highways Into Space*). If you've read any of those books, I hope you'll enjoy reading stories about some of the same subjects they wrote about from a different perspective.

Over the years, I've developed friendships with people around the world who are interested in space exploration. Many of them are students or in the early stages of their careers. I'm often asked during presentations and interviews what advice I would give to someone who is interested in a career at NASA, or anywhere else in the rapidly growing commercial space industry. My most frequent answer to that question is, "If there's a job you want, or something you want to do, go for it! Don't be afraid to fail. Be more committed to your dreams than you are to your comfort zone." I know that is easier said than done, but you should not let a fear of rejection or failure prevent you from applying for the job you want.

A good example of this: Ron McNair, one of the astronauts who died in the *Challenger* accident, was selected by NASA in the first group of Space Shuttle astronauts in 1978. He and some other Navy pilots went to Patuxent River Naval Base for a weekend. While there, Ron met Charlie Bolden, who was in the Naval Test Pilot School. They talked and, before Ron left, he asked Charlie, "Hey, are you going to apply for the space program?" Charlie said, "No," and Ron asked, "Why not?" Charlie replied, "Ron, they'll never pick me." Ron said to Charlie, "That's the dumbest thing I've ever heard. How do you know if you never ask?" He took Ron's advice and submitted an application. Charlie was selected in the next astronaut class in 1980 and, in 2009, was appointed by President Barack Obama as the NASA administrator.

"Failure is not an option" is an iconic phrase heard around NASA. That's a perfectly good mantra if you're working to save the lives of three astronauts trying to return to Earth in a severely damaged spacecraft, as was the case with Apollo 13. However, in your daily life, there is nothing wrong with an occasional failure. You've probably heard the phrase, "If you're not failing, you're not trying hard enough."

NASA has suffered many failures over its history, but after each one, it has come back even stronger and more committed to continuing its exploration of space.

It is now 2024. NASA had a successful uncrewed Artemis I launch in late 2022 and is planning a crewed mission that will orbit the Moon, but not land on the lunar surface, in late 2025. The success of the Artemis Program to date, along with my desire to promote STEM engagement and education, has motivated me to make a serious attempt at this book-writing thing.

Another motivation is to prove that you're never too old to learn a new skill. I am now 72 years old, and I have never taken a writing course, let alone written a book. Another of my favorite quotes to live by is, "If you want something you've never had, you must do something you've never done."

You may have heard some of the stories in this book, but I guarantee you haven't heard all of them. So, if you are reading this, I hope you will enjoy and possibly learn something from those stories about my adventures with NASA over the past 50-plus years.

Herb Baker

1 - A Lucky Coincidence

I believe that growing up a few miles from where a NASA center would be built was one of the luckiest things to ever happen to me. I'm convinced my life would have been very different—and not nearly as exciting—had I not grown up in that place at that time.

Herb's father (at lower left on his back) working on an aircraft engine at Ellington Air Force Base

I'm named after my father, Herbert H. Baker, Sr., who served in the Air Force and Air Force Reserve for 27 years and was stationed at Ellington Air Force Base (AFB) in South Houston, where he worked as an aircraft mechanic. During the 1950s and 1960s, he would often take our family to Ellington AFB for air shows and open house events. Coincidentally, fifty years later, the office I managed at Johnson Space Center (JSC) supported NASA's Aircraft Operations organization at

Ellington. As part of that job, I made many trips back to the same airstrips and hangars I had visited as a kid. Dad passed away in 1991, so the memory of those sights and smells at Ellington was an emotional experience for me whenever I visited there.

I often think of two life philosophies my father preached to me. The first was, "A turtle has to stick his neck out if he's ever going to get anywhere." That one was easy to understand. The second was, "It doesn't matter where you get your appetite, as long as you eat at home." I had to think about that one for a while.

Our family of seven lived in a small house in South Houston until 1960, when we moved into a larger house with a huge yard in League City, a small town about 15 miles to the south, just outside the Houston city limits.

* * *

President John F. Kennedy gave his "We choose to go to the Moon…" speech at Rice Stadium in September 1962. Just one month after his speech at Rice University, the president was dealing with the Cuban Missile Crisis.

I had recently started the fifth grade at League City Elementary School, where we did "duck and cover" drills. I still have the memo, dated October 24, 1962, from our school district which we took home to our parents, describing the school's plans in case of an attack on the mainland.

The most frightening paragraph from the memo stated, "Should the time come that any long-range missile is fired to the mainland of the United States, or the Gulf Coast mainland is shelled; or on orders from Civil Defense or other competent authority, schools will be immediately dismissed and buses will start for home as rapidly as safety permits. Schools would resume operation on subsequent days with an all-clear report."

During this time, the United States was in the early stages of building a space program and would soon open the Manned Spacecraft Center (now the Johnson Space Center), seven miles from our home in League City. The 1962 NASA appropriations bill included approval for a "manned spaceflight laboratory." NASA Administrator James Webb appointed a team of four men, one of whom was Ed Campagna, to help with the site selection for that new NASA facility.

Ed was the construction engineer for the Space Task Group (STG), which had been based at the Langley Research Center in Hampton, Virginia. The STG would transition to the new Manned Spacecraft Center (MSC) in Houston. Ed was also a professional magician. I would later become friends in high school with both his son, Larry, and his daughter, Pam (or "PJ"), who lived in Nassau Bay—a new community built across the street from MSC where many of the astronaut families lived.

The criteria for selection of the new space center site included "access to water transportation by large barges, a moderate climate, availability of all-weather commercial jet service, a well-established industrial complex with supporting technical facilities and labor, close proximity to a culturally attractive community in the vicinity of an institution of higher education, a strong electric utility and water supply, and at least 1,000 acres of land."

Initially, MacDill AFB in Tampa, Florida, was the preferred site of the selection team because the Air Force was planning to close its Strategic Air Command operations there. The Houston site had been the second choice. Before the final selection and announcement were made, the Air Force decided not to close MacDill, removing it from consideration. Houston became the preferred location, and a public announcement of the newly selected Houston site was made on September 19, 1961.

Ed Campagna was happy with the selection of Houston over a retired Air Force Base since they would now be starting a center with new equipment and new concepts and not be burdened with old utility systems and worn-out equipment that wasn't suited for a mission like NASA's.

MSC would open in 1963 and held its first open house for the public on June 6, 1964. That same year, I entered the seventh grade at Clear Creek Junior High in Webster, TX, just two miles from MSC. It was the only junior high school in the community.

By that time, NASA had selected the first three groups of astronauts, and most had moved their families to the rapidly growing community near our home. Most of the children of the astronauts that were my age were now my school classmates.

* * *

On October 31, 1964, the NASA astronaut corps suffered its first fatality. Ted Freeman, who had been selected as an astronaut in the third group of astronauts a year earlier, was flying home from St. Louis. As he approached landing at Ellington AFB, a goose flew into the left-side air intake of his NASA jet, damaging the engine.

As he tried to land, he realized he was short of the runway and might hit nearby military housing, so he turned his plane away from that direction. He ejected, but his parachute didn't open in time and he died upon impact. The Clear Lake City-County Freeman Branch Library near JSC is named in his memory.

* * *

In 1967, soon after getting my driver's license at age 15, I started my first job, during the summer months, at a service station in Webster. In those days, it was called a service station rather than a gas station because the gas pumps were not self-service as they are today.

If you pulled your car into that Enco (part of the Humble Oil Company which merged with Standard Oil to become Exxon) station and asked for a "fill-up," we would pump your gas, clean the outside of your windows with a wet chamois cloth, and then ask if you wanted us to check your engine oil level, fill your tires with air, and even vacuum the interior of your car. I'm not making that up.

Gas cost about thirty-five cents per gallon. We had a vending machine inside the building that dispensed candy bars for five cents each. During that summer and the following summer, I worked ten hours per day, seven days a week, for $50. That works out to $0.71/hour, but I was happy to have that job.

A few years later, I spent a couple of summers working as a ride operator at the Astroworld amusement park adjacent to the Astrodome. That job was much more fun than working at a service station and, at $1.65 per hour, paid much better.

* * *

As a lover of sports, I played Little League baseball from the time I was eligible until I outgrew the Pony League at 15 or 16 years old. I also joined the track team and football teams when I went from elementary school to junior high school in the seventh grade.

Looking back at the roster for that 1964 seventh grade football team I played on, there are three names that jump out— Fred Borman, son of Apollo 8 astronaut Frank Borman, Jay

Carpenter, son of Mercury 7 astronaut Scott Carpenter, and Bill King, who 51 years later, in 2015, narrowly lost a runoff election for Mayor of Houston to Sylvester Turner. Bill is a Houston attorney and businessman and is still active in local politics.

THE 1964 CLEAR CREEK FOOTBALL ROSTER "COUGARS"	7th Grade	
	White	Maroon
1. Herbert Baker	48	
2. Mike Bannister	55	
3. Tim Barcelona	69	
4. Lou Becker	63	
5. Allan Bopp	89	
6. Fred Borman	26	
7. Philip Caldwell	57	
8. Jay Carpenter	47	
9. Craig Cherry	63	
10. Bob Covert	52	
11. Johnny Cornelius	38	
12. Mike Dalton	56	

A portion of the Clear Creek Junior High 7th grade football roster from 1964 with photo of Herb (looking at camera) in his football uniform.

* * *

In addition to Fred Borman and Jay Carpenter being football teammates, Jan Cooper (daughter of Gordon Cooper), Scott Grissom, and Wally Schirra III, were also classmates at Clear Creek Junior High that year.

By the time I entered Clear Creek High School in 1967 as a sophomore, NASA had selected the first six astronaut groups. Clear Creek was still the only high school in the community, so most of the astronaut's children went to the same school.

When a classmate's father was flying on an Apollo mission (e.g., Donn Eisele on Apollo 7 or Frank Borman on Apollo 8) during that period, our high school newspaper would include an article about the mission. Otherwise, it wasn't something the students often talked about. As a fifteen-year-old kid, I had no idea at that time how much of an impact NASA would eventually have on my life.

HE'S RIGHT ABOUT HERE - Freshman Melinda Eisele, daughter of Astronaut Donn Eisele, points out to HILIFE reporter, Tina Depperschmidt, her father's approximate location. The Astronauts departed from Cape Kennedy last Friday and will return early next week. Photo by Bob Todd.

Article in the Clear Creek High School student newspaper featuring Melinda Eisele during Apollo 7 mission

"WHAT, YOU'RE A MATADOR" - Ed Borman, right, reacts to the Poster showing his brother Fred as a matador in the Madrid bull ring. The Two brothers recently returned to Clear Creek with interesting stories of Their three-week goodwill trip to numerous European cities.

Article in Clear Creek High School student newspaper from March 7, 1969, after Frank Borman & family returned from goodwill tour to several European cities following the Apollo 8 mission.

* * *

During high school, many of my friends were connected to NASA. Most had at least one parent that worked either for NASA as a civil servant or worked for a NASA contractor. Melinda Eisele, daughter of Apollo 7 astronaut Donn Eisele, and Mark Grissom, Gus's younger son, were both in the marching band with me, where we became friends. I've stayed in touch and seen them both recently. Mark is an Air Traffic Controller. His older brother, Scott, is a retired FedEx airline captain.

Another bandmate, Steve Sjoberg, is the son of Sig Sjoberg, who was the Director of Flight Operations at MSC for three years before becoming the deputy center director under Chris Kraft in 1972.

Another good friend and bandmate, Dave Andrich, is the son of Steve Andrich, who was Manager of the Flight Requirements Office for many years.

* * *

Ted Skopinski, the father of classmates Lorie and Teresa Skopinski, had worked with Katherine Johnson with the Space Task Group at Langley Research Center. He was instrumental in giving Katherine Johnson the credit she deserved for her contributions to calculating the mathematical equations required to launch and track spacecraft on orbital flights. John Glenn famously said, "If she says they're good, then I'm ready to go," referring to Katherine's calculations before his Friendship 7 flight in 1962.

Johnson's supervisor at that time had been reluctant to give her the credit she deserved for her work since at that point, no woman at NASA had ever had her name included as a contributor in such a report. Skopinski convinced her supervisor that she had done most of the work and should be given credit for it.

Johnson, and other women at NASA, would go on to have their names on many other reports. Skopinski helped break down that barrier. He would later become Chief of the Apollo Trajectory Analysis Section at MSC/JSC after moving to Houston.

* * *

By the time I was a senior at Clear Creek High School, other astronaut's kids in school with me included Eddie White, Faith Freeman, Carleen Gordon, Dionne Stafford, and Clay Bean.

2 - Apollo 1 Through Apollo 6

I have only vague memories of the Mercury and Gemini programs, starting with John Glenn's Friendship 7 flight on February 20, 1962 (about two weeks after my tenth birthday), and continuing until Project Gemini ended with the Gemini XII flight of Jim Lovell and Buzz Aldrin in November 1966. By that time, the Manned Spacecraft Center, built on land that had once been a cow pasture, had been open for three years and the surrounding community was growing rapidly.

* * *

Tragically, during the early evening of Friday, January 27, 1967, astronauts Gus Grissom, Roger Chaffee, and Ed White died in a fire on the launch pad. Chaffee's two children were a few years younger than I was, but Grissom's sons, Scott and Mark, and Ed White's son, Eddie, were school classmates. This was a difficult time for the entire community.

At the time of the accident, the preflight test activity on the launch pad was designated Apollo-Saturn 204 (AS-204), but it was later redesignated by NASA as Apollo 1. NASA did not designate any missions as Apollo 2 or Apollo 3. The first Saturn V launch became Apollo 4.

* * *

Apollo 4 and Apollo 5 were both uncrewed test flights. Apollo 4, launched in 1967, was the first Saturn V rocket flight, and Apollo 5, launched in 1968, was the first flight of a Lunar Module. An interesting note about the Lunar Module: In June 1966, the name was changed from its original designation,

Lunar Excursion Module (LEM), to simply Lunar Module (LM). NASA management felt that the word "excursion" made the program sound frivolous. Even after the name change from LEM to LM, nearly everyone pronounced LM as "lem" because it was easier than saying the letters individually.

The final uncrewed Apollo mission was Apollo 6, which was launched in April 1968 on a Saturn V. The flight gave NASA the confidence to use the Saturn V for crewed launches. After my mother passed away in 2007, I went through her photos and found a picture of her standing beside the flown Apollo 6 Command Module. I had never seen the photo and have no idea what the story behind it was.

Herb's mother, Alyene Baker, next to the Apollo 6 Command Module

* * *

I am still in touch with Scott and Mark Grissom and, in the summer of 2018, I spent some time with Mark at an event called "Galactic Gathering" in Gus's hometown of Mitchell, IN. It was a weekend filled with space-themed events that included tours of Gus's boyhood home and the Grissom Memorial Museum, which houses his Gemini III spacecraft. I also met one of Gus's brothers, Lowell, that weekend.

Gus Grissom's boyhood home in Mitchell, IN

Herb with Mark Grissom   *Herb with Lowell Grissom*

3 - Apollo 7 Through Apollo 10

The first crewed flight of the Apollo program was Apollo 7, which launched on October 11, 1968, and splashed down in the North Atlantic Ocean on October 22. The crew consisted of Commander Wally Schirra, making his third and final spaceflight, Command Module Pilot Donn Eisele, and Lunar Module Pilot Walt Cunningham (although Apollo 7 didn't carry a Lunar Module).

It was the first time three men flew together in space, and it was an important step leading to the Apollo 11 lunar landing just nine months later. This mission is probably as well-known for the tension between the crew and ground controllers during the flight as it is for the successful testing of the Command Module in low Earth orbit, which showed that it was capable and reliable enough for a three-man crew to travel to the Moon.

The problems with the mission started before liftoff. With offshore winds in Florida gusting above the maximum allowed for launch, Schirra didn't want to launch, but Flight Director Glynn Lunney convinced the team to launch anyway.

The launch went well, but the mission went downhill from there. On the second day, the crew had planned to do a live television broadcast, but Schirra, who had not wanted to do a broadcast, was suffering from a head cold and resisted at first. He later gave in and did the broadcast.

Eisele also developed a head cold and Cunningham was experiencing "severe discomfort," likely caused by motion sickness. Feeling unwell, the crew began criticizing the flight controllers, which angered NASA managers. The worst of the conflict came at the end of the mission when Schirra declared that the crew would not wear their helmets during reentry, as was normally required. He wanted to be able to blow his nose, as he was still suffering from a head cold.

NASA wanted the helmets worn to protect the crew in case of an accidental depressurization. Apollo 7 splashed down safely, with the crew not wearing helmets. The mission was considered a success, but the three astronauts never flew in space again. Schirra, Eisele, and Cunningham was the only crew from the Apollo/Skylab era not awarded the Distinguished Service Medal following their missions.

Forty years later in 2008, NASA Administrator Mike Griffin awarded the Distinguished Service Medal, NASA's highest award, to the crew. Griffin acknowledged the controversy surrounding the flight but felt that the achievements of the crew merited his reconsideration.

Thinking back to 1968, when I was a 16-year-old still in high school, I was not aware of the drama surrounding the Apollo 7 flight. Soon after the flight, Eisele divorced his wife and married a woman with whom he had been having an affair.

On a related note, of the twenty-one married astronauts who traveled to the Moon, eleven divorced.

* * *

My personal favorite of the Apollo missions came next: Apollo 8, in December 1968. It was the first time a spacecraft with humans aboard left low Earth orbit. The crew included Commander Frank Borman, Command Module Pilot Jim Lovell, and Lunar Module Pilot Bill Anders. They would be the first humans to witness, and photograph, an Earthrise.

Anders, describing the Saturn V launch, said, "The sideways shaking was unbelievable. The vibration was so intense that you couldn't see the instrument panel. I thought we'd had it during the launch. I was hoping Frank Borman didn't have his hand on the abort control. Frank said he took his hand off because he'd rather die than make a false abort."

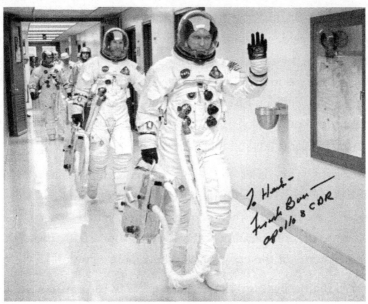

Apollo 8 crew on their way to the launch pad, led by Commander Frank Borman [NASA photo]

Apollo 8 took less than three days (68 hours) to travel to the Moon and orbited it ten times before returning to Earth. Their Christmas Eve television broadcast, during which they read the first ten verses from the *Book of Genesis* was, at that time, the most-watched TV program ever. The astronauts splashed down in the Pacific Ocean on December 27 and were later named Time magazine's "Men of the Year" for 1968.

1968 had been a difficult year. The U.S. was involved in the Vietnam War. There were heavy casualties in the war and protests here at home. Martin Luther King Jr. was assassinated in April. Robert Kennedy was assassinated in June. There were protests against the Vietnam War and riots at the Democratic

National Convention in Chicago. I heard Glynn Lunney say that, after the Apollo 8 mission, a woman sent a telegram addressed to the Apollo 8 crew that said, "Thank you for saving 1968." After everything that happened that year, it ended with the *Book of Genesis* being read from the Moon.

* * *

Apollo 9, flown in March 1969 in low Earth orbit, was the first flight of the full Apollo spacecraft: the Command and Service Modules with the Lunar Module. The crew consisted of Commander Jim McDivitt, Command Module Pilot David Scott, and Lunar Module Pilot Rusty Schweickart. It was the first crewed flight that included a Lunar Module. The LM tests were successful, clearing the way for Apollo 10 two months later.

Rusty Schweickart tells a story (excerpted from his JSC Oral History interview) describing how the Apollo 9 crew named their spacecraft:

"The naming of spacecraft was part and parcel of the program, and public relations and everything else, from the time the program started. Of course, on Mercury, everything got off on a big patriotic kick with *Friendship 7* and *Freedom 7*, and everything 7, you know. And I guess Gus' spacecraft was the *Liberty Bell 7*, if I remember.

So, when it came to the Gemini spacecraft, the same thing prevailed, and Gus, being the first up with Gemini III, named it the *Molly Brown*. And he named it the *Molly Brown* for somewhat obvious reasons, when he realized that the *Liberty Bell* sank, and, of course, the *Unsinkable Molly Brown*, etc. It was cute, and everybody appreciated it, but there were probably some raised eyebrows, naming it the *Molly Brown*. Well, Gus was a fairly stubborn character, and so he insisted on it being named *Molly Brown*, and that worked until Gus ended up with an illicit sandwich in space on Gemini III, and after that, the edict came down from NASA Headquarters that there would be no more names for spacecraft, that they would be Gemini and GT [Gemini-Titan]. Everything after that was names and numbers. So it became Gemini IV, Gemini V, VI, and VII, Gemini 67 for the combined mission, etc. And everything was numbers.

Well, here we are coming along with Apollo, and, of course, the first Apollo mission, forgetting the fire, became Apollo 7 with Wally and Donn Eisele and Walt Cunningham, and then Apollo 8, of course, went out around the Moon with Frank Borman, Jim Lovell, and Bill Anders. And then came Apollo 9. Fine.

So the logic was, well, we're Apollo 9. But now we've got two spacecraft, so when we're separated, what are we? And when talking to each other, are we Apollo 9 Alpha and Apollo 9 Bravo, or whatever? And then when I go outside on EVA, I'm sort of a third spacecraft because now we're communicating over the radio with three different things. So what am I, you know? Or am I just Rusty or what am I?

So at any rate, at one point McDivitt and I don't think Dave was there. I can't remember. At any rate, it was at the Fireside, which was a place in Downey, California, where we used to eat dinner and have drinks once in a while. We were sitting at the bar at the Fireside and we had a little discussion about this, and we decided we're going to start calling each other names. And we figured we can't make it anything humorous.

It's got to be something very obvious, bland, that nobody can complain about. But we needed to have call signs so that there wasn't going to be any ambiguity. Did somebody mishear a call from the ground and get the wrong suffix and do something wrong? We wanted clear and distinct names.

So we decided, and especially at that time because you'd look at the Command Module on the factory floor and it had a thin blue coating on it over the heat shield, and it looked like a gumdrop. Well, how can you complain about gumdrops? So it became *Gumdrop*. Of course, when you look at that [Lunar Module], I mean, what else does it look like but a spider? So, *Gumdrop* and *Spider*. Now, can anybody complain about *Gumdrop*? Well, we didn't ask anybody; we just started using it in the simulations.

As we got closer and closer to flight, Mission Control started using it. Then when I went outside, logical, right? *Red Rover*, because I had to cross over from one spacecraft to another. So, 'Red Rover, Red Rover, come over,' right? So it became *Red Rover*, *Gumdrop*, and *Spider*. We didn't ask anybody. We didn't tell anybody. We just started doing it, and it stuck. And from then on in Apollo, the names came back in. So that's the story of naming spacecraft."

* * *

Apollo 10, launched in May 1969, was the prelude to the first lunar landing. The crew, Commander Tom Stafford, Command Module Pilot John Young, and Lunar Module Pilot Gene Cernan, tested the spacecraft systems, but didn't land on the Moon. Stafford and Cernan separated from the Command Module and flew the LM within 8.4 miles of the surface. The crew orbited the Moon 31 times before splashing down on May 26, less than two months before Apollo 11 lifted off.

The Command Module was called *Charlie Brown* and the Lunar Module was called *Snoopy*. The names were taken from a popular comic strip at the time called Peanuts. The comic strip's creator, Charles Schulz, was reluctant to approve use of the names for the mission because, in the comic strip, Charlie Brown was constantly failing.

Snoopy has been associated with the space program for many years. Workers who perform in an outstanding manner may be awarded a Silver Snoopy pin. The Silver Snoopy is still awarded by NASA today and is typically presented to the recipient by an astronaut.

Tom Stafford pats the nose of Snoopy doll held by Jamye Flowers, with John Young & Gene Cernan following behind him.[NASA photo]

The morning of the launch, Jamye Flowers, a young woman who worked in the astronaut office, planned to prank

Gene Cernan by having someone tell Cernan that she wanted him to take something to the Moon for her. Cernan replied, "Sure. But at this point, the only thing I can do is put it in the pocket of my spacesuit. Get it down to me and I'll take it for her."

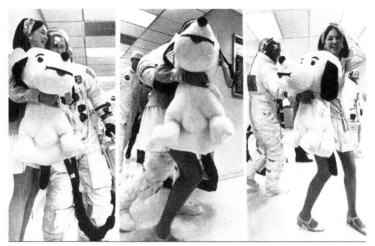

Jamye Flowers trying to prank Gene Cernan with a Snoopy doll [NASA photos]

Rather than something small enough to fit in a pocket, Jamye was holding a huge Snoopy doll as the suited astronauts walked down the hallway outside the crew quarters on their way to the launch pad. Tom Stafford walked by first and patted Snoopy's nose. As Cernan walked toward Jamye, rather than patting Snoopy, he grabbed Jamye and Snoopy and dragged them toward the elevator as if he was going to take them both to the Moon with him. He did let go of them before getting on the elevator.

4 - Apollo 11

July 1969 was during the summer between my junior and senior years in high school. I was 17 years old, had been driving for two years (at that time in Texas, you were allowed to get a driver's license at age 15 if you passed a driver education course). I had recently bought my first car, a 1966 Pontiac Tempest. It was an exciting time in the Clear Lake area surrounding the Manned Spacecraft Center.

After the five successful Apollo flights over the previous 15 months, we were eagerly looking forward to the first Moon landing attempt by Apollo 11, scheduled for that month.

Television networks from around the world began sending crews to Houston in early July to begin covering the Apollo 11 mission. The major networks—ABC, CBS, and NBC—sent crews from New York and set up temporary studios using reconfigured mobile homes parked on-site at the Manned Spacecraft Center.

My mother was hired by ABC News, which wanted someone who lived locally and was familiar with the area, to be the personal assistant for Jules Bergman. Bergman was the ABC Science Editor and had been covering NASA missions for ABC since the Mercury Program.

After ABC hired Mom, she helped me also get a job on-site as a "gopher" with Metromedia, one of the other TV networks that had set up shop at MSC to cover Apollo 11. During the mission, I worked for both ABC and Metromedia.

Herb's mother with ABC Science Editor Jules Bergman in the ABC studio at MSC

Because the Internet didn't exist and digital video wasn't widely used until the 1980s, any film of interviews, press conferences, and other activities had to be physically transported to television studios in New York for broadcast. The most important part of my job was to make the 100-mile round trip to Houston's Intercontinental Airport twice every day to drop off canisters of film to be flown to New York.

That took only a few hours each day, so I also did other odd jobs like ripping the news from the teletype machine, picking up documents from NASA's Public Affairs Office (e.g., transcripts of news conferences, printouts of the Mission Commentary, Flight Plans, Press Kits, photos, maps) that were provided for use by the media.

Working on-site at the Manned Spacecraft Center as a teenager was such a thrill that I would have probably done the job without pay. Not only were the TV networks paying me $2.50 an hour, they provided me with a rental car that I could use 24/7 since they wanted me to be "on call" in case there was breaking news to cover. And, of course, there was a constant flow of astronauts, flight directors, and other NASA managers coming into our studio to be interviewed.

I was working on-site that Wednesday morning, July 16, 1969, when Apollo 11 launched at 8:32 a.m. Houston time. I watched the launch on a small black and white TV in the ABC-TV studio at MSC. Four days later, I listened to the coverage of the July 20 lunar landing on the radio in my car shortly after 3 p.m. local time, as I was making one of my many trips up I-45 to Houston Intercontinental Airport to drop off film.

Because I was often away from the studio, I didn't meet all the people who came by for interviews, but I did get photos of at least three—Apollo astronauts Alan Shepard, Pete Conrad, and Dave Scott—all of whom walked on the Moon.

Herb's mother with Alan Shepard in the ABC studio at MSC

Top photo: Herb's mother with with Pete Conrad; Bottom photo: Dave Scott with NBC-TV employees

* * *

Years later, I heard Gene Kranz talk about being the Flight Director for that first lunar landing. He said everyone in Mission Control took their final restroom break before they locked the doors. When they returned, he gave them a pep talk and finished by saying, "I will stand behind every decision you make. We came into this room as a team and we will leave as a team." They locked the doors, and he said, "The doors won't be opened until we've either landed, crashed, or aborted." Those were the only three possible outcomes that day.

The average age of the guys in that room was 26 years. Gene said, "We didn't know it at the time, but it was going to be an extremely challenging landing." They were having communication and computer problems and he said they landed with somewhere between 17 to 47 seconds of fuel remaining.

Prior to the launch, the Apollo 11 astronauts were interviewed by the press. When Armstrong was asked whether he'd be taking any personal mementos with him to the Moon, he replied, "If I had a choice, I would take more fuel."

After landing, the mission control team couldn't take a break because they had to go through a series of "Stay/No Stay" decisions—one at two minutes, one at eight minutes, and one at two hours. Those times were fixed to allow for the Lunar Module to rendezvous with the Command Module with its available fuel.

One of Apollo 11's computer problems, as the LM was descending towards the surface, was the guidance computer giving 1201 and 1202 alarms at an altitude of about 6,000 feet. Just 11 days before the launch, a NASA simulation supervisor, or SimSup, had put the flight controllers, including Steve Bales, Jack Garman, and Capcom Charlie Duke, through a simulation that intentionally caused a 1201 alarm. Dave Scott and Jim Irwin, the backup crew for Apollo 12 and the prime crew for Apollo 15, were the astronauts participating in the simulation. Bales aborted the landing that day because the team had been unable to determine how to respond to the 1201 and 1202 alarms.

APPLICABLE TO: IN DESCENT, AVERAGE-G ON

ALARM CODE	TYPE	PRE-MANUAL CAPABILITY	MANUAL CAPABILITY
00105 MK ROUT. BUSY	POODOO	PGNCS GUID. LOST, *PGNCS/AGS ABRT/AERT STG (decision how on current rules) (NO LR DATA)	PGNCS GUIDANCE N0/60 (PGNCS GO for TAPE METER, CROSS-POINTERS, CONTROL, ABORTING) (NO LR DATA)
00430 CANT INTG. S.V.	"		
01103 CCSHOLE-PROG. BUG	"		
01204 NEG. WAITLIST	"		
01206 DSKY, TWO USERS	"		
01302 NEG. SQ. ROOT	"		
01501 DSKY, PROG. BAD	"		
01502 DSKY, PROG. BUG	"		
00607 LRHB, NO SOLN	"		
"O.F." = Overflow, too many. CONTINUING OCCURRENCE OF:		DUTY CYCLE MAY DEGRADE PGNCS (AGS CONTROL MAY HELP - SEE BELOW) (WATCH FOR OTHER CUES) PGNCS CONDITION UNKNOWN, DSKY MAY BE LOCKED UP, DUTY CYCLE MAY BE UP TO POINT OF MISSING SOME FUNCTIONS (NAV. LAST TO DIE) SWITCH TO AGS (FOLLOW ERR NEEDLES) MAY HELP (REDUCES PGNCS DUTY CYCLE SIGNIF.)	SAME AS LEFT (except "other cues" which would otherwise be cause for ABORT PROBABLY AREN'T, INSTEAD IT WOULD BE PGNCS GUIDANCE N0/60 - COMPLETE MANUAL LANDING IN AGS.)
01104 DELAY ROUT. O.V.	BAILOUT		
01201 EXEC. O.F. (VAC)	"		
01202 EXEC. O.F. (JOBS)	"		
01203 EXEC. O.F. (TASKS)	"		
01207 EXEC. O.F. (HKS)	"		
01210 TWO USERS	"		
01211 MRK ROUT. INTRPT	"		
02000 DAP O.F.	"		
ISS WARNING WITH:		PIPA/CDU/IMU FAIL DISCRETES PRESENT (Other mission rules suffice; alarm may help point to what rule will be broken)	same as left
00777 PIPA FAIL	LIGHT ONLY		
03777 CDU FAIL	"		
04777 PIPA, CDU FAIL	"		
07777 IMU FAIL	"		
10777 PIPA, IMU FAIL	"		
13777 CDU, IMU FAIL	"		
14777 PIPA, CDU, IMU FL	"		

Portion of Jack Garman's handwritten 'cheat sheet' of all the possible computer error codes [NASA photo]

Flight Director Gene Kranz instructed Bales to write down every possible computer alarm and what might happen. Bales gave the assignment to Garman. When the 1201 and 1202 alarms occurred during the landing, Garman, Bales, and Duke recognized them instantly.

Jack Garman passed away in 2016. Shortly before, I had a chance to talk with him about his involvement in the events of July 20. One of Jack's two daughters, Jenny Arkinson, was a co-worker of mine at JSC. I was sitting with Jenny at a luncheon one day and Jack joined the group at our table.

I had been curious about what would have happened if Jack hadn't been so well-prepared for the computer alarms that occurred as Armstrong and Aldrin were approaching their landing. Would mission control have aborted the landing as they had that day during the simulation? I asked Jack what he thought about that scenario, and he replied: "I think at that point, when the alarms started, Neil was taking that baby all the way down to the surface, regardless of those alarms."

A few years later, I attended an Astronaut Scholarship Foundation event where one of Armstrong's sons, Rick, spoke and he was asked the same question. Rick's answer was similar to Jack Garman's. Rick said, "I believe if mission control had called for an abort, my dad's response would have been 'What's that, Houston? You're breaking up… having a hard time hearing you. Say again. I didn't copy that…'"

Jack Garman also described what it was like as Apollo 11 touched down on the Moon. He had watched hundreds of simulated landings, which seemed real to him, but on this real one, he heard Buzz call out, 'We've got dust now,' something he had never heard before. He said that he thought to himself when he heard Buzz's words, "Oh, my gosh, this is the real thing, isn't it?"

* * *

I remember watching the black-and-white images of Neil Armstrong stepping off the Lunar Module's ladder on television. An estimated 650 million people watched the broadcast on Earth. Apollo 11 was one of the most historic events of the twentieth century.

In 1961, when President Kennedy declared that we would go to the Moon, NASA had no idea how to do that. They didn't have rockets, launchpads, or spacesuits. They didn't have a list of what they needed and didn't even know what they didn't know. They didn't know what they would find when they got to the Moon or if the astronauts would be able to function effectively in space. Some people thought the Lunar Module might sink into the lunar soil upon landing.

Chris Kraft, the man who invented Mission Control, whom I met and briefly worked for while he was at the Johnson Space Center, said, "When [Kennedy] asked us to do that in 1961, it was impossible. We made it possible."

Another example of NASA's uncertainty was the Lunar Module. As the *Eagle* Lunar Module prepared to descend to the lunar surface on Apollo 11, the lander had never flown so far from the Command Module *Columbia*.

The Lunar Module had never landed on the Moon; in fact, it had barely landed on Earth. The Lunar Module was designed for one purpose—to land on the Moon. It wasn't designed to fly in Earth's atmosphere or gravity. The Moon has one-sixth of the gravity of Earth and has no atmosphere.

The Lunar Landing Training Vehicle (LLTV) was a follow-on to the Lunar Landing Research Vehicle (LLRV). LLTV-3 is suspended from the ceiling in the lobby of the Teague Auditorium at JSC.

There was no effective way to simulate flying the Lunar Module on Earth for testing. Learning to fly it was even harder than doing something like learning to drive a boat without being on the water. NASA developed what they called the Lunar Landing Research Vehicle (LLRV) to simulate Moon landings, but its test flights didn't always go well.

In May 1968, one year before Apollo 11 landed, an LLRV flight experienced a serious malfunction and crashed. The pilot had to eject to save his life. That pilot was Neil Armstrong.

* * *

The computing power of today's cell phones exceeds that of the computers in the Apollo spacecraft. The astronauts used paper star charts and a sextant to take star sightings to cross-check the computer navigation. In fact, a significant amount of work was done by hand during the Apollo Program. The heat shield was applied to the spacecraft by hand with a caulking gun. The parachutes were also sewn and then folded by hand. Despite its high-tech reputation, it's easy to forget how much of the lunar mission was handmade.

* * *

One of the men working at a console in Mission Control during that mission, Ed Fendell, handled the Command Module and communications with Kranz's team.

On the afternoon of July 20, Ed thought they would attempt to land on the Moon but wasn't sure it would happen. He described that day as surreal. When his shift was over, he went home and got some rest. He ate breakfast at a place called the Dutch Kettle before heading back to work the next day.

While there, a few men walked in and sat nearby. They were talking about the lunar landing and about their experiences fighting in Europe during World War II. One of the guys said, "Yesterday was the proudest I've ever been to be an American." Ed heard that and it suddenly hit him what they had done.

Ed says that even though he had been there in Mission Control, it wasn't until then that he fully realized what they had accomplished and what it meant to the country.

Today, Ed and I are both members of the NASA Alumni League-JSC, so I see him often.

* * *

After Armstrong and Aldrin had completed their spacewalk and returned to the Lunar Module, Aldrin noticed a switch lying on the floor amidst the lunar dust from their boots and realized it was the ascent arming switch/circuit breaker that had been accidentally broken off. Needing some way to complete the circuit to lift off and rejoin Collins in the CM, they notified Mission Control of the problem.

A Call from the Moon

While the astronauts were walking on the moon, George Peskuric of Apollo Systems, Houston, was off-duty and at home. The time was 1:20 a.m., July 21. The phone rang. Charles Humes, a GE engineer was calling from Apollo Systems End Item Control Center, one element of Reliability and Quality Assurance support to NASA's Mission Control. The caller said the astronauts, when re-entering the Lunar Module, had found the knob on a circuit breaker critical to the startup of the ascent engine had been broken off. Mr. Peskuric, an expert in lunar module electrical power systems, was asked: "Could the breaker with a broken knob be successfully engaged?" Mr. Peskuric proceeded to the control center to pour over reliability experience and quality support documents. Now as the astronauts slept, GE employees worked to submit a preliminary report at 5:30 a.m. The record search continued and a final report was passed through Richard Peverley, the prime LM-5 End Item Engineer, to NASA by 8:30 a.m. The report stated that in every case where a knob had been broken off the circuit breaker was successfully engaged. The message was relayed to the astronauts and the attempt to close the breaker in Eagle was made. It meant a normal engine firing sequence and liftoff would be successful. For GE men concerned, the suspense was over. The astronauts were coming home.

Article in a GE company newsletter regarding the broken ascent arming switch on the Apollo 11 Lunar Module

Aldrin eventually came up with the idea to insert a felt-tipped marker he had with him into the small opening where the switch should have been, but not before engineers on the ground had worked on the problem overnight. One of those engineers was the father of John Peskuric, one of my high school friends. George Peskuric was awakened by a phone call at 1:20 a.m. and spent the night studying the situation and writing a report stating that, "… in every case where a knob had been broken off, the circuit breaker was successfully engaged."

* * *

In August that year, I attended Houston's Salute to NASA and Apollo 11 at the Astrodome. Robert Gilruth, Director of the Manned Spacecraft Center from 1961 to 1972, spoke at the event hosted by Houston Mayor Louie Welch. Jack Valenti, president of the Motion Picture Association, introduced Frank Sinatra, who sang *Fly Me to the Moon*. Actor Bill Dana, who created the fictional astronaut character José Jiménez, performed that evening as well.

* * *

One of my favorite baseball stories involves Apollo 11. Gaylord Perry, a member of the Baseball Hall of Fame, was a starting pitcher for the San Francisco Giants from 1962 to 1971. (He also pitched for seven other Major League teams before retiring in 1983.) Like most pitchers, he was not a good hitter.

One day in 1963, while watching him take batting practice, his manager, Alvin Dark, joked, "There will be a man on the Moon before Gaylord Perry hits a home run." Six years later, on the afternoon of July 20, 1969, one hour after Apollo 11 landed on the Moon, Perry hit his first career home run.

* * *

In September, I received a letter from ABC with a reimbursement check for use of my personal car to deliver film to Houston Intercontinental Airport while covering Apollo 11. (And, yes—I did cash that check. $21.90 was a lot of money to me back then!)

American Broadcasting Company

1330 AVENUE OF THE AMERICAS · NEW YORK, N. Y. 10019

LT 1-7777

Sept. 19, 1969

Mr. Herbert Baker
P.O. Box 961
League City, Texas

Dear Herbert,

Enclosed please find a check in the amount of $21.90. This is in payment for use of your own car during the Apollo Eleven coverage. The amount is based on your reported 219 miles at 10¢ per mile.

Thank you, very much for your help and please excuse our delay in payment.

Sincerely,

Jerry Myers
ABC - TV
Unit Manager

Letter from ABC reimbursing Herb for use of his personal vehicle while covering the Apollo 11 mission

Herb with the Apollo 11 Command Module "Columbia" which was temporarily on display at Space Center Houston in 2017

Herb sitting at the ABC studio desk with his friend, Chuck Sebek, on-site at MSC. Chuck had a similar job with a different TV network

5 - Apollo 12

In November 1969, a few months after the Apollo 11 mission ended, I was hired by NBC-TV to support its coverage of the Apollo 12 mission, which would launch on November 14. That mission got off to a scary start because the vehicle was struck by lightning 36.5 seconds after it lifted off from the launch pad. The electrical discharge disrupted the Signal Conditioning Electronics (SCE) unit, resulting in a loss of telemetry. Without the telemetry data, there was no way for flight controllers to know the condition of the spacecraft.

The discharge also caused the spacecraft's three fuel cells to be disconnected from the power buses, causing them to go offline and leaving the Command Module operating with only backup battery power. The backup battery power would last only two hours. The alarm system sounded and almost every warning light on the control panel in the Command Module came on.

Gerry Griffin, in his first mission as Flight Director, faced the possibility of aborting the flight if they couldn't solve the electrical problem. An abort would have involved jettisoning the spacecraft with the three astronauts aboard, followed by blowing up the Saturn V rocket.

John Aaron, who was 26 years old, was sitting at the Electrical, Environmental and Consumables Management (EECOM) console in Mission Control. He recognized the garbled telemetry pattern he was seeing on his monitor from a simulation a year earlier. Griffin likely expected Aaron to call for a mission abort, but Aaron made a different call. He told

Griffin to tell the crew to "try SCE to Aux," which meant flipping the Signal Conditioning Electronics switch to its auxiliary (AUX) power supply.

Herb sitting at the CSM EECOM console in the Apollo Mission Control Room where John Aaron made the call "SCE to AUX" to save the Apollo 12 mission after the vehicle was struck twice by lightning

When Aaron made the call, neither Griffin nor Capcom Jerry Carr recognized the switch he was referring to. Pete Conrad's response was "What the hell is that?" However, Alan Bean remembered the SCE switch from a training event a year earlier when a similar failure had occurred during a simulation.

Bean flipped the switch as Aaron suggested, and it worked. The telemetry was restored. Shortly after that, the fuel cells were reconnected to the spacecraft power buses. An abort would not be necessary after all. Fortunately, the lightning strikes had not caused serious damage. John Aaron and Alan Bean had saved the mission and, possibly, the Apollo Program. Aaron became known by his colleagues as a "steely-eyed missile man."

* * *

Bean was not initially assigned to Apollo 12. He was selected as an astronaut in 1963 and served as the backup Command Pilot for Gemini 10 in 1966, but did not receive an early Apollo flight assignment. Instead of an Apollo assignment, he was assigned to the Apollo Applications Program, which eventually led to Skylab.

Clifton 'C. C.' Williams was assigned to the backup crew for Apollo 9, joining Pete Conrad, who was the backup commander for that flight. As was customary, the backup crew for Apollo 9 would become the prime crew for Apollo 12. According to Bean, Conrad had initially asked for Bean for his backup crew but was told that Bean was not available and was asked to pick someone else. Conrad picked Williams but Williams was later killed in a crash of his NASA T-38 jet in October 1967 while en route to visit his parents in Mobile, AL. This gave Conrad, who had been Bean's instructor at the Naval Test Pilot School, the opportunity to request that Bean replace Williams as a prime crew member on Apollo 12. His request was granted.

* * *

The Apollo 12 Moon landing was so precisely executed that they landed within walking distance of where Surveyor 3, a lander sent to sample lunar soil, had landed two years earlier. Surveyor 3 remains the only probe visited by humans on another celestial body.

* * *

My most memorable assignment covering Apollo 12 occurred on the final day of the mission, November 24, 1969, when I was sent with a cameraman to Pete Conrad's home in Timber Cove, four miles from the Manned Spacecraft Center, to film his family watching the Command Module splash down in the Pacific Ocean that afternoon. My memories of that day, being in the Conrads' living room while the cameraman filmed the family watching their television set, are so vivid that it seems as though it was yesterday. Splashdown occurred just before 3:00 p.m. local time.

Because this was a human-interest story for the Houston area rather than national news, the film was to be delivered to a local television studio near downtown Houston rather than being flown to New York.

I remember walking into the dining room in the Conrads' home with the cameraman after he finished filming. He removed the film from the camera, placed it in a canister, and handed it to me.

I made the short drive back to NASA with the film, where a helicopter was waiting for me. The local TV station was so eager to get the film for their 5:00 p.m. news show that they chartered a helicopter to fly me and the film the 27 miles from NASA to their studio, instead of having me deliver it by car.

I suppose they were afraid I might get lost, have an accident, run out of gas, get stuck in traffic, or experience some other calamity that would prevent me from delivering the film quickly enough. The helicopter flight, which took only ten minutes, was my first ride in a helicopter. After I strapped myself in, the pilot told me he had just returned from flying missions in Vietnam.

Even though that day was more than 50 years ago, I remember running from the helicopter into the building with the film and handing it to a woman who was waiting for me, behind a long counter in the lobby. The odd thing is that I don't recall anything after that moment—not even the helicopter ride back to my car at NASA. I suppose the adrenaline that had been flowing through my body for the previous couple of hours had suddenly dissipated once I delivered the film.

6 - Apollo 13

Apollo 13, which lifted off at 13:13 Houston time on April 11, 1970, would be my third consecutive mission working for the news media. A popular movie about Apollo 13, directed by Ron Howard, was released in 1995, telling the story of the mission on the big screen. In the spring of 1970, after two consecutive successful lunar landings, many Americans likely expected Apollo 13 to be another routine Moon landing.

That was true for the first fifty-six hours of the flight. Then, on April 13, Command Module Pilot Jack Swigert was asked to activate the stirring fans in the cryogenic oxygen tanks. Shortly after stirring the oxygen tanks, the astronauts heard a loud bang and Swigert said to Mission Control those now famous words: "Okay, Houston, we've got a problem here." Capcom Jack Lousma in Mission Control responded: "This is Houston, say again, please." Commander Jim Lovell calmly interjected: "Houston, we've had a problem."

The third member of the crew was Lunar Module Pilot, Fred Haise. I've heard him speak about his experiences on this flight many times over the years.

Fred said the explosion sounded like a loud, echoing sound because they were in a vehicle with metal hulls, like a big tin can, and it sounded as if someone had hit them with a sledgehammer. The explosion happened soon after a TV broadcast from inside the Lunar Module. If the explosion had happened a short time earlier, the crew would have been live on TV.

APOLLO 13 MISSION COMMENTARY 4-13-70 CST 9:00P GET 55:48:00 169/1

      CAPCOM   13, we've got one more item for you when you get a chance. We'd like you to stir up your cryo tanks. In addition have shaft and trunion
      SC   Okay.
      CAPCOM   for looking at the Comet Bennett if you need it.
      SC   Okay, stand by.
      SC   Okay, Houston. Hey, we've got a problem here.
      CAPCOM   This is Houston, say again please.
      SC   Houston, we've had a problem. We've had a main B bus interval.
      CAPCOM   Roger. Main B interval. Okay, stand by 13 we're looking at it.
      SC   Okay, right now, Houston, the voltage is looking good. And we had a pretty large bang associated with the caution and warning there. And if I recall, Main B was the one that had a amp spike on it once before.
      CAPCOM   Roger, Fred.

APOLLO 13 MISSION COMMENTARY 4-13-70 CST 9:00P GET 55:48:00 169/2

      SC   In the interim here, we're starting to go ahead and button up the tunnel again.
      CAPCOM   Roger.
      SC   Yes. That jolt must have rocked the sensor on C NON and O2 quantity 2 it was oscillating down around 20 to 60 percent, now it's full scale high again.
      CAPCOM   Roger.
      SC   And Houston. We had a restart on our computer, we have PGNCS light and the restart and reset.
      CAPCOM   Roger. Restart and PGNCS light.
      SC   Okay. And we're looking out our service module RCS helium one. We have B is manifold and P is manifold, helium two D is manifold and secondary propellants I have A and C manifold. T mag temperatures. Okay AC two is showing zip. I'll try and reconfigure on that.
      CAPCOM   Roger.

END OF TAPE

Mission Commentary from shortly before the oxygen tank explosion until shortly afterwards. (Note: the transcriber erroneously typed "main B bus interval" when it should have been "main B bus undervolt")

41

The thrusters, which control the spacecraft, were firing when they normally wouldn't. Fred knew something bad had happened but, at the time, he didn't realize how bad it was. He and Lovell started drifting from the Lunar Module, where they had been for the TV broadcast, toward the Command Module (CM). When they got there and looked at the instrument panel, they were confused because seven warning lights and the master alarm were all on.

When Fred realized they had lost oxygen tank #2, he felt sick to his stomach, knowing that, rather than landing on the Moon, they needed to return home as soon as possible. He had trained as the backup Lunar Module Pilot for Apollo 8 and Apollo 11, doing all the work that the prime crews did, and he realized his opportunity to land on the Moon was gone. Years after the mission, Fred was asked in an interview if there was ever a time that he feared they wouldn't make it home safely. He replied, "Candidly, you don't know if you can get back even before you go."

The astronauts powered down the CM and all three crew members moved into the LM. I heard Fred tell a story about how the LM was different in many ways from the CM: "There were lots of steps taken to make the LM lightweight, and it made different noises. You could hear pumps making a gurgling sound, the cabin fan running, and other noises like that. Jack Swigert was worried because he had never been inside a Lunar Module in his life. He was the CM expert and had lived with the development of the CM while with North American Aviation as an engineering test pilot.

At one point, Swigert asked, "Do you think this thing will make it?" He was worried about all the strange sounds he was hearing. Fred told Swigert, "Well, all that gurgling and stuff you hear—only worry if you stop hearing it."

For astronauts flying to space, it is customary to designate another astronaut to take care of their wives and kids, at least administratively, if they don't make it back. Jerry Carr, a fellow Marine who lived around the corner from Fred in El Lago, served that role for him. He invited Jerry to his house to show him where all the important paperwork was before the mission. However, Fred never reached a point during the mission where he felt they had lost all hope. He says that he always had confidence they would make it back.

Apollo 13 went around the far side of the Moon at about 131 miles of altitude—roughly double that of a normal mission, which entered lunar orbit at 60 miles altitude. This gave them a broader view of the Moon. The crew held the record in the *Guinness Book of World Records* for being the furthest people from Earth at that time—because of the higher altitude and partially because the Moon's orbit is elliptical; and when they got to the Moon, it was further away from Earth. Fred admitted he would have preferred to land rather than hold that record.

Apollo 13 crew arriving on their recovery ship, USS Iwo Jima, by helicopter
[NASA photo]

Without retelling the whole story of Apollo 13, the crew successfully powered down the Command Module and used the Lunar Module as a lifeboat to safely return to Earth. Some people have called the mission NASA's "most successful failure."

The title of Fred's recently released book, *Never Panic Early*, is analogous to a Mission Control principle regarding problems that come up unexpectedly: "Don't do anything to make it worse." The idea is to take the time to study the problem and assess what should be done rather than acting hastily and making the problem worse.

On the return trip, Fred ate only peanuts, cubed cookies, and cubed bread because the food requiring hot water was frozen solid, and no hot water was available.

Mirror from Apollo 13 presented to flight controllers now hanging on the wall in the Apollo Mission Control Room

The crew couldn't take many objects out of the LM to bring back home because they were using it until the last possible minute. But they did take a mirror, now mounted on a plaque on the wall in Mission Control [with a typo in the message—grateful is spelled 'greatful']. The plaque reads: "This mirror, flown on Aquarius, LM-7, to the moon April 11-17, returned by a greatful Apollo 13 crew to 'reflect the image' of the people in mission control who got us back!"

Since the crew wasn't seeing the news every day, they didn't realize how the entire world was closely following the drama unfolding on their flight. Fred joked that after returning home, meeting people, and appreciating the emotion the world experienced while following their mission, he felt that "maybe he had missed something being up there."

The crew was encouraged to see the positive public reaction to their safe return home. They had worried that the problems experienced on their mission might result in a loss of faith in the U.S. space program.

The day after the crew safely returned home, splashing down in the Pacific Ocean on April 17, President Nixon awarded the Medal of Freedom to the Mission Operations Team during a ceremony at MSC.

Because it was a Saturday, I was able to attend the event with a few of my high school friends. After the award ceremony, President Nixon and the astronauts' families flew to Hawaii to meet the crew. Nixon presented the Medal of Freedom to the crew at a ceremony at Hickam Air Force Base in Hawaii.

I heard Glynn Lunney, one of the Flight Directors for Apollo 13, speak in 2015 about a meeting the day after the Apollo 13 accident, during which he had to brief senior NASA leaders on five options for the crew's return. He expected a lengthy meeting with difficult questions. After he gave his recommendation on what he felt was the best option, and answered one question from Deke Slayton, NASA Administrator Thomas Paine stood up and said, "I have only one question: What can we do to help you men?" Glynn replied that he had all the support he needed and the meeting was over.

Herb with Glynn Lunney at the Johnson Space Center

Lunney said that he thought about the meeting often over the years and appreciated how Paine had trusted him and his team. He called Paine "quite a man and quite a leader."

The LM *Aquarius* burned up in the atmosphere after being jettisoned just before the crew's reentry. Understandably, Fred has a soft spot in his heart for *Aquarius* and thought she had been magnificent. He would later write, in an article for *Life* magazine, that he wished *Aquarius* also had a heat shield because, he said, he would "like to have that LM sitting right in my backyard."

* * *

One of my duties for the TV networks I worked for was regularly pulling the news coming in on the UPI teletype or TWX (TeletypeWriter eXchange) machine. The machines were huge electric typewriter-like devices that printed news on long, continuous rolls of paper that could be torn off at any point. The heat from the machine, combined with the ink, created a distinct smell that I still recognize to this day. It doesn't happen often, but occasionally I smell that same odor, and it immediately takes me back 55 years.

I've saved many of those TWXs. This one is from April 14, shortly after the oxygen tank explosion, and discusses whether the number 13 is lucky or unlucky.

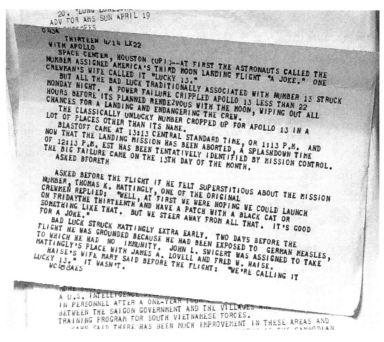

UPI story Herb pulled from a teletype/TWX machine while working for ABC-TV the day after the oxygen tank explosion on Apollo 13.

The TWX message reads:

"At first the astronauts called the number assigned America's third Moon landing flight 'a joke.' One crewman's wife called it 'Lucky 13.'

But all the bad luck traditionally associated with number 13 struck Monday night. A power failure crippled Apollo 13 less than 22 hours before its planned rendezvous with the Moon, wiping out all chances for a landing and endangering the crew.

The classically unlucky number cropped up for Apollo 13 in a lot of places other than its name.

Blastoff came at 13:13 Central Standard Time, or 1:13 p.m. and now that the landing mission has been aborted, a splashdown time of 12:13 p.m. EST has been tentatively identified by Mission Control. The big failure came on the 13th day of the month.

Asked before the flight if he felt superstitious about the mission number, Thomas K. Mattingly, one of the original crewmen replied: 'Well, at first we were hoping we could launch on Friday the thirteenth and have a patch with a black cat or something like that. But we steer away from all that. It's good for a joke.'

Bad luck struck Mattingly extra early. Two days before the flight, he was grounded because he had been exposed to German measles, to which he had no immunity. John L. Swigert was assigned to take Mattingly's place with James A. Lovell and Fred W. Haise.

Haise's wife Mary said before the flight: 'We're calling it Lucky 13.' It wasn't."

* * *

I've heard Fred say that he liked the *Apollo 13* movie and thought that Ron Howard did a good job directing it, in part because Tom Hanks was constantly pushing Howard to make it as realistic as possible, like getting NASA to let them use the KC-135 aircraft to achieve weightlessness for about 25-30 seconds at a time to film many of the scenes in the movie.

Before filming started, Bill Paxton, who played Fred in the movie (and who wasn't particularly interested in space exploration), visited KSC, where Fred took him on a tour of the center. He took Paxton on a tour of the new Space Station facility that had just been built. None of the hardware had been delivered to the building yet, but Fred took him down into some underground tunnels where there were gaseous and electrical lines (for testing hardware) that would come up through the floor. Fred said that Paxton looked around and said, "Wow. This is where I should have filmed *Aliens*."

Fred also said that Paxton told him he was worried because this role would be the first time he was playing someone in a movie that was still alive. His other roles had been fictional characters (or historical characters). Fred told him, "Don't worry. It's only a six-day event, not the life story of Gandhi. You'll do fine."

* * *

In addition to the Mission Commentary I collected while working the Apollo missions, I also saved many other documents offered to the news media by the NASA Public Affairs Office, including photos, Press Kits, and Flight Plans.

Sample of the documents, photos, and patches collected by Herb while covering the Apollo 13 mission in Houston

* * *

Fifty years after their flights, the Apollo 11 and Apollo 12 missions celebrated their 50th anniversaries with parties and galas around the country. As luck would have it, the COVID-19 pandemic struck in early 2020. This led to the postponement or cancellation of in-person events planned to celebrate Apollo 13's 50th anniversary in April of that year.

7 - Apollo 14

After Apollo 13 was unable to explore the Fra Mauro crater in the lunar highlands as planned, it was chosen as the landing site for Apollo 14. Before the Apollo 13 landing was aborted, Apollo 14 was scheduled to land near Littrow Crater in Mare Serenitatis. After Apollo 13 returned, the decision was made for Apollo 14 to land in the Fra Mauro formation, which was considered scientifically more important. The crew, consisting of Commander Alan Shepard, Command Module Pilot Stu Roosa, and Lunar Module Pilot Ed Mitchell, launched on January 31, 1971. Their launch had been postponed due to the Apollo 13 investigation.

* * *

After working for the news media covering the three previous Apollo missions, I was unable to support the Apollo 14 mission because I had started my freshman year at the University of Texas a few months earlier and was attending classes in Austin.

* * *

There's an interesting backstory about how Alan Shepard was assigned to the Apollo 14 crew. After his successful Freedom 7 flight in 1961, he had been selected as the commander for the first crewed Gemini mission. During training for that flight, he began experiencing dizziness and nausea and was eventually diagnosed with Ménière's syndrome. He was removed from flight status and given a desk job as Chief of the Astronaut Office.

51

He was determined to find a solution so he could fly again and eventually tried a new procedure that cured his condition. At that point, NASA returned him to flight status, and he went to Deke Slayton, asking to be assigned to Apollo 13. He tells the story in an interview for the JSC Oral History Project:

"When NASA finally said I could fly again, I went to Deke and said, 'We have not announced publicly the crew assignment for Apollo 13. I have a recommendation to make.' I had picked two bright, young guys—one of them a Ph.D., and one of them a heck of a lot smarter than I was—and made up a team to go for an Apollo flight. I said, 'I would like to recommend that I get Apollo 13, with Stu Roosa as command module pilot and Ed Mitchell as lunar module pilot.' Deke said, 'I don't know. Let's try it out.'

So we sent it to Washington, and they said, 'No, no way.' So we said, 'Now wait a minute. Shepard's got to be at least as smart as the rest of these guys, maybe a little smarter.' And they said, 'Well, we know that. But it's a real public relations problem. Here this guy's just gotten un-grounded and all of a sudden, boom!, he gets a premier flight assignment.' So then the discussion went on for several days and finally they said, 'All right, we'll make a deal. We'll let Shepard have Apollo 14. Give us another crew for Apollo 13,' and so that's what happened."

* * *

After separating from the Command Module, Apollo 14's Lunar Module, *Antares,* encountered two potentially serious problems during its descent to the surface. The first was an abort signal caused by a faulty switch in the Lunar Module. This was resolved by tricking the system into thinking an abort had already occurred.

Another problem occurred when the Lunar Module's radar was unsuccessful in locking onto the lunar surface, which deprived the navigation computer of Lunar Module altitude and vertical descent speed data. This was resolved by cycling the radar's breaker.

* * *

I'm intrigued by something Shepard once said about being a Navy test pilot and carrier pilot, and how he enjoyed the challenge of being able to control a new vehicle in a new environment as an astronaut. Shepard said, "It's something I had been doing for many, many years as a Navy pilot, as a carrier pilot, and believe me—it's a lot harder to land a jet on an aircraft carrier than it is to land a Lunar Module on the Moon. That's a piece of cake, that Moon deal!" Spoken by someone who did both.

* * *

For some, Apollo 14 is remembered for Shepard swinging at two golf balls with a makeshift "golf club." He missed on the first swing but exclaimed that the second ball went "miles and miles and miles." It was the last thing he did before climbing up the ladder to come home.

Before playing golf on the Moon, Shepard needed approval from his boss, MSC Center Director Bob Gilruth. This is that story (from his JSC Oral History Project interview):

"So far I'm the only person to have hit a golf ball on the Moon. Probably will be for some time. And being a golfer, I was intrigued before the flight by the fact that a ball with the same club head speed will go six times as far. Its time of flight—I won't say 'stay in the air,' because there's no air—its time of flight will be at least six times as long. It will not curve, because there's no atmosphere to make it slice. And I thought, 'What a neat place to whack a golf ball!' Well, when I went to Bob Gilruth to tell him I wanted to hit a couple of golf balls, [he said] there was absolutely no way.

I explained that it was not a regular golf club; it was the handle that we use that we pulled out with a scoop on the end to scoop up samples of dust with. That was already up there to be thrown away. Then we had a club head which I had adapted to snap on this handle and two golf balls, for which I paid: the two golf balls and the club at no expense to the taxpayer.

The thing that finally convinced Bob was when I said, 'Boss, I'll make a deal with you. If we have screwed up, if we have had equipment failure, anything has gone wrong on the surface where you are embarrassed or we are embarrassed, I will not do it. I will not be so frivolous. I want to wait until the very end of the mission, stand in front of the television camera, whack these golf balls with this makeshift club, fold it up, stick it in my pocket, climb up the ladder, and close the door, and we've gone.' So he finally said, 'Okay.' And that's the way it happened."

* * *

Stu Roosa took several hundred tree seeds with him in the Command Module on Apollo 14, in honor of his days with the Forest Service. The seeds were germinated and planted after their return to Earth. The seedlings were distributed around the world as commemorative Moon trees.

8 - Apollo 15

The Apollo 15 mission occurred during the summer of 1971, from July 26 to August 7. The crew consisted of Commander Dave Scott, Command Module Pilot Al Worden, and Lunar Module Pilot Jim Irwin. I was on summer break from school, so I was able to cover that mission, working for NBC.

This was the first Apollo "J mission," which had greater hardware capabilities and a larger scientific payload capacity than earlier missions. They were also the first to use the Lunar Roving Vehicle (LRV) and the first to stay on the lunar surface for nearly three full days. The LRV included a camera that could be remotely controlled by Flight Controller Ed Fendell in Houston.

I heard Gene Kranz tell a story about a medical issue on this mission. Kranz said, "The crew had been on the surface for two days, doing three spacewalks, and had reached a state of extreme dehydration. Their blood chemistry had changed. Their blood was depleted of potassium, which is essential for normal heart function. The problem was that the flight surgeon didn't tell me we had a problem. He was treating the crew on the spacecraft as his patients as opposed to treating me as one of the team, so that I would know what was going on."

"Jim Irwin had this problem on the surface and then we had the same problem with both crewmen during powered flight coming back up to rendezvous with the Command Module. As the crew was transferring from the LM into the CM, they were not doing tasks in the correct order."

"It was in the debriefing after that shift when I found out about that problem. This led to a come-to-Jesus meeting with our flight surgeons, and they became members of our team from that day forward."

Herb in the NBC-TV studio with co-workers at the Manned Spacecraft Center during coverage of the Apollo 15 mission

* * *

Alone in the Command Module, Al Worden completed a burn to place the Command Module in a higher orbit around the Moon. Due to the position of Apollo 15's landing site, Worden's lunar orbit was 27 degrees higher than that of other Command Module Pilots, who orbited near the lunar equator.

After the mission, Worden was presented with a Guinness World Record certificate for being the "Most Isolated Human in History" for being farther away from his crewmates on the lunar surface and from the people on Earth than anyone had ever been, while he was on the far side of the Moon.

He was also presented with a Guinness World Record certificate for performing the "First Spacewalk in Deep Space," which he completed to retrieve film cassettes from cameras in the Scientific Instrument Module (SIM) bay of the Service Module.

* * *

Worden retired from NASA in 1975. In 1982, he ran for Congress in Florida's 12th congressional district. Although he lost in the primary, he considered his run as one of the high points of his life. He remained involved in the space community, serving as chair of the Astronaut Scholarship Foundation's board of directors from 2005 to 2011. He was a joy to be around, lighting up every room he entered. He was also a tireless supporter of STEM (Science, Technology, Engineering, & Math) education.

9 - Apollo 16 And Apollo 17

Apollo 16, launched on April 16, 1972, was another "J mission," characterized by more extensive science, a longer stay on the lunar surface, and use of the Lunar Rover. The crew consisted of Commander John Young, Command Module Pilot Ken Mattingly, and Lunar Module Pilot Charlie Duke.

For Mattingly, it was his first spaceflight after being removed from the crew of Apollo 13 due to his exposure to rubella (German measles), although he did not contract the disease. It was Duke's only spaceflight. Duke was just 36 years old—the youngest of the 12 astronauts to walk on the Moon.

The call sign chosen by Young and Duke for the Lunar Module was *Orion*, and the call sign chosen by Mattingly for the Command and Service Module was *Casper*, named for Casper the Friendly Ghost, a popular animated cartoon character of that era. Mattingly quipped that he chose the name *Casper* for the CSM because he felt, "there are enough serious things in this flight…"

Of all the Apollo lunar missions, the largest sample returned to Earth, known as "Big Muley" and weighing 26 pounds, was collected by Young and Duke on this mission.

After their final spacewalk, Duke placed two items on the surface: a photograph of his family, encased in plastic, and a commemorative medallion issued by the U.S. Air Force, celebrating its 25th anniversary in 1972. The back of the photo was signed and read: "This is the family of Astronaut Duke from Planet Earth. Landed on the Moon, April 1972"

Herb with Apollo 16 Lunar Module Pilot Charlie Duke

* * *

A story from Apollo 16 that I've heard Charlie Duke tell is about a lost wedding ring. At some point on their way to the Moon, Ken Mattingly misplaced his wedding ring. They would normally find small items they had lost in the Command Module after several days because the items would collect in the air filters. By the time they were on their way home on the ninth day of the eleven-day mission, Mattingly had given up trying to find the ring and had started thinking of excuses to tell his wife.

On that ninth day, Mattingly was in the middle of an 83-minute spacewalk to retrieve film cassettes from cameras in the SIM (Scientific Instrument Module) bay of the Service

Module, with Duke keeping an eye on him from the Command Module hatch as a safety observer. Duke had turned to head back inside when he noticed a small object, slowly floating out of the hatch. He tried to grab the ring with his gloved hand but missed. "Well, lost in space," he thought to himself.

They were traveling at a high speed, but since they were all moving together with no wind resistance, it seemed as though they were just floating. As Duke watched the ring float away, he saw that it was headed for the back of Mattingly's helmet. The ring hit his helmet and bounced back directly towards Duke, who was still at the hatch. The odds of a round ring hitting a round helmet and bouncing back exactly 180 degrees in the opposite direction are almost zero—but that's exactly what happened. When the ring eventually reached Duke, he grabbed it with one of his gloved hands. Against nearly impossible odds, Mattingly's wedding ring was saved.

* * *

Besides Duke, Pete Conrad and Stu Roosa were known to be country music fans. Conrad, Roosa, and Duke were friends with Bill Bailey, a popular country music radio DJ in Houston. Before Duke left on his mission, he called Bailey and told him that he needed two hours of country music and asked him to record a cassette tape for him.

On the crew's first break after leaving Earth orbit, Duke plugged in the cassette and the first thing he heard was, "My name is Merle Haggard. I want to dedicate this especially to Charlie Duke. He was the one who asked for the tape and, of course, the other two fellas are invited to listen, unless you have separate compartments, maybe you can get away from it. And we hope you all get back safely."

The next thing he heard was an original song written especially for him by Randy Rogers and Robert Earl Keen, titled *"Charlie Duke Took Country Music to the Moon."* The lyrics included a verse, "Well, he was backup man on the flight that burned out—you know the one they made the movie about—but he got his chance on Apollo 16."

* * *

Duke was once asked, "What is it like to stand on the Moon and look down to see Earth?" He replied, "When you're standing on the Moon and you look down, you see your feet, just like you do on Earth."

* * *

Duke spent 11 days in space on Apollo 16. He tells the story of how his travel voucher (yes, astronauts who fly in space are required by the Government to file a travel voucher) showed travel from Houston to KSC, to the Moon, to the Pacific Ocean, and back to Houston. He said the Temporary Duty (TDY) rate was $25 per day, for which he would have been reimbursed $275, but since "government quarters and meals" were furnished, those costs were deducted. He says he got a check for $13.75 in travel expenses for that 11-day trip.

* * *

In 2011, 39 years after the Apollo 16 mission, it was in the news again. In 2006, Hurricane Ernesto flooded parts of Pamlico Sound in southeastern part of North Carolina. An 11-year-old boy was walking around his family's beach home neighborhood shortly after the storm, with lots of debris still scattered around. There was a metal sheet on the ground and when he turned it over, there was an Apollo 16 logo on it.

The boy's family contacted NASA about the find. It took five years for NASA to confirm that the metal was from the first stage of Apollo 16's Saturn V rocket. NASA asked the family to return the metal sheet and when they did, NASA gave them an all-access tour through the Kennedy Space Center and VIP-viewing of the final Shuttle launch, STS-135, in 2011.

* * *

Apollo 17, the final mission of the Apollo program, launched on December 7, 1972, with a crew of Commander Gene Cernan, Command Module Pilot Ron Evans, and Lunar Module Pilot Harrison "Jack" Schmitt. They landed at Taurus-Littrow, a mountainous area of the Moon.

It was the only nighttime launch of the Apollo Program and was the final crewed Saturn V launch. It was estimated that 500,000 people watched the launch in the Kennedy Space Center vicinity, despite it occurring shortly after midnight local time, and the launch was visible as far away as 500 miles.

The Apollo 17 launch was scheduled for December 1972 because Nixon did not want to risk a disaster impacting his re-election campaign, with the election occurring in November.

The mission was the longest of the lunar landing missions, lasting 12 ½ days. It also set a record for the longest spacewalk distance from the LM, with the crew traveling 4.7 miles from their spacecraft on one of their spacewalks.

As a member of the Apollo 14 backup crew, Joe Engle had been in line to be the Lunar Module Pilot on Apollo 17. When Congress canceled the Apollo 18 and 19 missions, NASA decided to assign a geologist rather than a pilot to this final mission. Schmitt, who had been scheduled to fly on Apollo 18, was selected to replace Engle.

* * *

The call signs assigned by the crew were *America* for the Command Module and *Challenger* for the Lunar Module.

Cernan and Schmitt performed three spacewalks and collected 254 pounds of rocks, the largest of which weighed almost 18 pounds. After completing their final spacewalk, Cernan parked the Lunar Rover about 170 yards from the LM, from where it would televise their liftoff several hours later. The lunar rover carried a television camera that was controlled remotely from Houston by Flight Controller Ed Fendell, from his Integrated Communications Officer (INCO) console in Mission Control.

The Apollo 17 ascent stage lifts off from the Moon [NASA photo]

NASA had tried, unsuccessfully, to capture video of the Lunar Module liftoffs for both Apollo 15 and Apollo 16. The tilt mechanism motor had burned out on Apollo 15 so the camera did not pan up as the Lunar Module accelerated upwards. On Apollo 16, the lunar rover was parked too close to the Lunar Module so, even though the camera worked perfectly, when the Lunar Module lifted off, it was quickly out of view of the camera. Fortunately, it all worked flawlessly for Apollo 17, with the camera capturing the Lunar Module's ascent stage lifting off from the lunar surface.

Herb's mother, Alyene Baker, with ABC News correspondent Jim Kincaid in the ABC-TV studio at Manned Spacecraft Center covering an Apollo mission

One of the ABC News on-air correspondents I met covering the later Apollo missions was Jim Kincaid. He had started with ABC in 1969, reporting in Vietnam at the height of the war. He suffered a broken back after being shot down in a military helicopter while in Vietnam. He spent several months recovering in a hospital in Hong Kong before returning to cover the space program in Houston.

10 - Skylab

A short five months after the Apollo Program ended, NASA launched Skylab 1 on May 14, 1973, on a modified Saturn V rocket. The vehicle was seriously damaged during launch, losing its micrometeoroid heat shield and one of its two primary solar panels. The remaining solar panel failed to deploy when debris from the lost heat shield became tangled in it, significantly reducing Skylab's available power.

The plan had been to launch the station, followed the next day by the first crew, referred to as Skylab 2. However, without its heat shield, Skylab was experiencing heat of approximately 125°F inside the Workshop, which made it uninhabitable. In addition, NASA managers were concerned that the excessive heat might cause the off-gassing of toxic chemicals, that the pre-positioned food might spoil, and that the photographic film might be ruined.

Mission Controllers at JSC developed an approach to temporarily manage Skylab's attitude to minimize exposure of the station to the Sun's rays to reduce the overheating problem while allowing Skylab to optimize its power generation. Engineers and astronauts at both JSC and the Marshall Space Flight Center worked around the clock studying options to replace the missing heat shield along with a plan to deploy the remaining solar array through use of a spacewalk.

Several options were considered by Skylab program managers for replacing the heat shield. The primary criteria were that it had to be small enough to fit inside the Command Module; ready in time for the crew launch; and not require a spacewalk to deploy. Jack Kinzler, Chief of the Technical Services Division at JSC (and the father of my high school friend, Nan Kinzler), developed a plan to use an umbrella-like parasol constructed of aluminum poles and a thin fabric made of nylon ripstop and aluminized mylar.

The parasol would be passed through a scientific airlock in the Skylab Workshop, located directly below where the missing micrometeoroid heat shield had been. It would then be opened like an umbrella and pulled down against the outside hull of the station to protect it from the Sun's radiation.

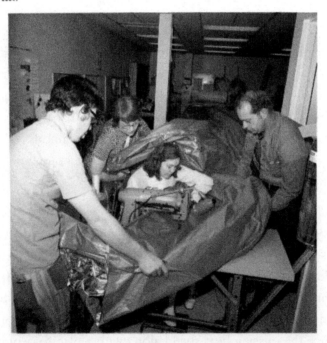

NASA
S- 73- 26047

Official NASA photo of Herb's mother, Alyene Baker, sewing the Skylab parasol with help from L to R – Dale Gentry, Elizabeth Gauldin, & Jim Barnett, Jr. [NASA photo]

My mother, Alyene Baker, who at the time was working as a seamstress for General Electric (GE), the NASA contractor responsible for providing space flight "soft goods" (i.e., fabric-based materials) to JSC, was chosen to do the sewing required to fabricate the parasol.

View of the parasol after it was deployed by the Skylab 2 crew in orbit
[NASA photo]

It amazes me that, within ten days, the parasol was designed, manufactured, tested, flown to Kennedy Space Center, and stowed aboard the Skylab 2 Command Module the night before its launch on May 25, 1973.

Kinzler, who also designed the U.S. flags that Apollo astronauts planted on the Moon and the "golf club" used by Alan Shepard on Apollo 14, received NASA's Distinguished Service Medal for his work on the parasol.

Mom rarely talked about her role in sewing the Skylab parasol, thinking it was no big deal—just part of her job. I remember her bringing home scrap pieces of that orange-colored parasol fabric. We lived in an old house with no air conditioning and she taped pieces of that fabric into some of our windows. I'm sure that we were the only house in the neighborhood using the same material used to lower the temperature in Skylab to cool our home.

The timing of these events, in mid- to late-May 1973, was fortunate for me as I had just finished my junior year at UT Austin and was able to return to Houston to continue my work with the news media covering the Skylab 1, 2, and 4 launches at JSC.

* * *

The first crew (Skylab 2) launched on May 25, 1973, and consisted of Commander Pete Conrad, Pilot Paul Weitz, and Science Pilot Joe Kerwin. As they approached Skylab, they saw that, as suspected, the micrometeoroid heat shield and one solar panel were missing, and the other solar panel was only partially deployed.

The crew moved from the Command Module into the Workshop the next day to begin activating it. It was approximately 125°F inside but, fortunately, there were no toxic gases. The crew's first job was to assemble the parasol. It took several hours and the crew took breaks in the Command Module to escape the heat of the Workshop. After assembly, it was pushed through the scientific airlock, opened like an umbrella, and pulled flush with the area of the missing heat shield.

The temperature began to drop and within three days was down to a more comfortable 82°F. Once this task was completed, they finished activating the station and began work on their science experiments, but that work was hindered by the limited power due to the jammed solar panel.

Meanwhile, Rusty Schweickart, who was the backup commander for Skylab 2, was leading a team to develop procedures to free the jammed solar panel. The first attempt, a stand-up spacewalk by Paul Weitz, was unsuccessful. A second attempt, on their 14th day in orbit, involved both Conrad and Kerwin conducting a spacewalk and using a cutting tool at the end of a long pole to cut the strap that was blocking the solar panel.

They were able to free the stuck solar panel on that spacewalk. When the panel suddenly deployed, both astronauts were flung away from the station but, because they were attached to strong safety tethers, they were able to return to their positions and complete the spacewalk. Had they not successfully freed the solar panel, there would not have been sufficient power on the station for the following crews to perform their planned experiments.

The Skylab 2 crew spent 28 days in space gathering solar and Earth science data, conducting medical experiments, and completing several other tasks before returning to Earth on June 22, 1973. Their 28 days in space were twice as long as the previous U.S. record.

* * *

The Skylab 3 crew of Commander Alan Bean, Pilot Jack Lousma, and Science Pilot Owen Garriott launched five weeks later. The initial plan had been for the Skylab 3 crew to also spend 28 days in space, but this was extended to 56 days after the success of the Skylab 2 mission. Of the many observations and experiments performed by this crew, one of my favorites was the spider web experiment.

The purpose of the experiment was to determine whether spiders could spin the same webs in space as they do on Earth. After launch, the two spiders, Arabella and Anita, were released into a box resembling a small window frame. It took a while for the spiders to adapt to weightlessness, but they were both able to build webs.

Arabella was able to spin a web on the first day, but it was incomplete. She completed another web on the second day, but it was neither as symmetrical nor as thick as those on Earth. However, after about 10 days in space, Arabella had adapted well to weightlessness. There's a brief conversation in the transcribed mission commentary between Science Pilot Owen Garriott (SPT) and the Capcom, Hank Hartsfield, (CC) that illustrates this:

"SPT   Say, Hank. You may remember, last night I told you I took down Arabella's web and put it around the little end of a swab so I could - so we could bring it back home and have it for ground analysis later on. Well, last night, she really did herself in. She spun the prettiest web that she's ever come up with. It would do grace to any sort of spider's den back on Earth.

CC   Roger. We copy.

SPT   Fills the full little cage, from corner to corner, all the way across, with nice circles and radials and everything the way you would expect one to spin it in one-G. Now, how she did it is another question. None of us were - have ever been around to watch her work. But she managed to get them all done, just as if there were gravity around to help her."

Unfortunately, both spiders died during the mission, possibly due to dehydration. An interesting result of the experiment was that the extensive media coverage showed that there was much interest across NASA, and the rest of the world, in experimenting on living organisms in space.

The spider experiment was one of 19 student experiments conducted on Skylab as part of a nationwide contest. More than 3,400 proposals were submitted to the Skylab Student Experiment Project by students across the U.S. After review by NASA, 19 of the submitted projects, covering a wide range of subjects, were considered suitable for Skylab's environment.

* * *

Another student experiment on Skylab was the Motor-Sensory Performance experiment, developed by my classmate Kathy Jackson at Clear Creek High School. Kathy proposed a test to measure the potential degradation of the crew's motor-sensory skills in weightlessness through the use of a hand-eye coordination test.

CBS Anchorman Walter Cronkite performing the Motor-Sensory Performance experiment with the experiment's creator Kathy Jackson [NASA photo]

The test was a device with 119 holes in a maze connected by straight lines. The astronauts had to insert a probe into the holes in sequence, following the pattern of the maze. The test was used to measure visual perception and motor response by recording the amount of time required to go through the maze, as well as the time required to move from hole to hole.

Each member of the Skylab 4 crew performed the test early in their mission, at the midpoint, and again toward the end. The crew enjoyed this test and wished they had more time to work with it. They performed well on the test with no change in their hand-eye coordination over the course of their mission.

According to a study, the participating students felt that their experience had made a positive impact on their lives and future careers. Kathy Jackson, who I am still in touch with, is a professor of educational technology at Penn State University.

Another of the student experimenters, Robert Staehle, is a manager at the Jet Propulsion Laboratory in Pasadena, CA. NASA continues today to involve students through educational programs on the ISS.

* * *

As of today, NASA has sent approximately 2,200 animals to space, including spiders, insects, monkeys, rabbits, and rats. In 1998, NASA sent 2,000 animals to space on one flight, the STS-90 Neurolab mission. Neurolab included snails, mice, rats, crickets, and two types of fish. The purpose of these experiments was to better understand the brain and central nervous system's response to these animals living in microgravity.

* * *

The Skylab 3 crew splashed down about 230 miles southwest of San Diego on September 25, 1973. Their 59 days in orbit were more than twice as long as the previous 28-day record.

The reason this mission lasted 59 days, instead of the planned 56, was that flight controllers calculated that, based on the orbital path, splashdown in the Pacific Ocean would have been about 1,000 miles west of San Diego if they returned on day 56.

However, if they waited three additional days and came home on day 59, the splashdown would occur less than 250 miles from San Diego and reduce the long trip to shore aboard the recovery ship.

The three-day extension seemed to be the smart thing to do, and the crew was happy to stay an additional three days, but there was one minor problem. I've often heard Jack Lousma describe this problem and its solution.

There was no washing machine, of course, on Skylab. The crew had coveralls that they would wear for two weeks and then trash them by tossing them out of the airlock. They would change their underwear—which Lousma referred to as 'skivvies'—every two days.

For the planned 56-day mission, each had 4 pairs of coveralls and 28 changes of underwear. That meant, following their normal routine, they would have no change of underwear for the additional three days.

The crew called Mission Control to let them know of their problem. After a brief wait, Mission Control called them back and told them: "Don't worry, guys. We've got a solution to your problem, but it's good news and bad news. The good news is that you're going to get to change your underwear. The bad news is, Alan, you change with Jack; Owen, you change with Alan; and Jack, you change with Owen."

* * *

The Skylab 4 crew of Commander Jerry Carr, Science Pilot Ed Gibson, and Pilot Bill Pogue launched on November 16, 1973. All three were flying in space for the first time. Carr was the first rookie astronaut to serve as a commander since Neil Armstrong on Gemini 8 in 1966. The crew completed many important scientific studies of Earth and the Sun.

They accomplished all of the mission objectives, including medical studies, astronomical observations, Earth resource studies, and four spacewalks. They returned home after a mission of 84 days, splashing down in the Pacific Ocean on February 8, 1974. This set a record for the longest spaceflight, which stood until 1977, when it was broken by the Soviets. No American astronaut would spend that much time in space again until 1995.

* * *

Photo signed by the Carr family children [NASA photo]

In 1979, a few years after the Skylab 4 crew returned home, I became active in community theater and performed in several shows with three of Jerry Carr's children—Jamee, Jessica, and Josh. The Carr family hosted some wonderful cast parties after several of our theater performances at their home in El Lago.

We have remained friends over the years, and in 2023, I asked all six of the Carr children sign a family photo for me. The photo was an official NASA photo I had saved from 1973 while I was working with ABC covering the Skylab missions.

* * *

Prior to Skylab, the longest period that humans had been in space was 22 days. Sadly, that crew—three Soviet cosmonauts on the Soyuz 11 mission in 1971—were found dead in their capsule after they returned to Earth. A problem with a seal in their capsule caused their cabin to depressurize, leading to the deaths of all three from asphyxiation.

Afterward, Soviet officials initially gave no explanation of what caused the accident, except to say that it was being investigated by a government commission. It was the upcoming joint venture between the U.S. and the USSR that led to the disclosure of the cause of the Soyuz 11 accident. The two countries were planning the joint Apollo-Soyuz Test Project (ASTP), however, before the U.S. would participate in that program, NASA wanted to understand the cause behind the deadly Soyuz 11 mission.

Some U.S. space experts speculated that the cosmonauts had exceeded human limitations in space and that the prolonged weightlessness had played a role in their deaths. But if that were true, all three men would have most likely not died at the same time. In addition, the cosmonauts were in good health and had not complained of any troubling effects due to living in microgravity.

The Soviets eventually provided detailed reports from their post-flight investigation and the steps they had taken to make sure the failure would not happen again.

* * *

Part of the Earth resources work done during the Skylab missions was a program called multistage sampling. A few years ago, I moderated a panel discussing Skylab at Space Center Houston with former Flight Director Bill Reeves, who had been involved in this activity. He described how the multistage sampling was done: Whenever Skylab would be making a pass over the U.S., aircraft operations personnel on the ground were in communication with the Mission Control Center who would give an anticipated pass time a day ahead, and a flight crew and an airplane would be moved to a staging base nearby.

They would time it so that the aircraft would be flying when Skylab passed overhead and they would take photos and record sensor data of the same target that Skylab was observing.

In addition, there were instances when personnel were doing inventories or studies (e.g., crop disease) on the ground at the same time. There would also be a helicopter flying overhead using sensors and cameras to record data. There would be a P-3 aircraft flying at around 20,000 feet with cameras and sensors, a C-130 aircraft at 30,000 feet, a high-altitude aircraft (such as a WB-57) at 60,000 feet, along with Skylab in orbit.

The observations would be timed such that they were all focused on the same target at the same time. This allowed them to obtain all of the imagery with the same lighting conditions. It was the first time anything like this had been done. This work was a precursor to the development of Earth resources satellites, which is how we have Google Earth today.

* * *

Crews on all of the previous Gemini, Apollo, and Skylab missions had been instructed not to take pictures of a certain part of central Nevada, known years later as Area 51. The area was home to the Groom Lake air base, where aircraft such as the U-2 and SR-71 were tested. The Skylab 4 crew forgot about these instructions and had taken several photos of the area. NASA could have simply deleted them from the Skylab imagery archive, but each photo had a specific sequential frame number.

There was concern that by deleting them, someone reviewing the images might notice the missing numbers and start asking questions. With the large number of photos taken, JSC center director Chris Kraft felt that there was a better chance that the unauthorized images might go unnoticed—and that's exactly what happened. Skylab's photos of Area 51 went unnoticed for 40 years.

* * *

It was hoped that the upcoming Space Shuttle program could be used to visit Skylab and restore its usefulness. After the last Skylab crew departed, NASA depressurized Skylab, stabilized its position, and deactivated most of its onboard systems. Still, there was hope that Skylab could be saved. NASA considered a mission to boost Skylab to a higher orbit during one of the Shuttle's Orbital Test flights. Among the flight crews planned for those flights were Fred Haise and Jack Lousma.

NASA had approved the development of a Teleoperator Retrieval System (TRS), a remote-controlled device that could potentially rescue Skylab. The TRS, an uncrewed space vehicle with propellant tanks and engines, was planned to be flown on the third Shuttle mission. After release from the Shuttle, the TRS "tug" would be manually flown by Lousma with controls from the Orbiter cockpit rear panel, from several hundred feet away, to a docking with Skylab. The Shuttle crew would then execute a small maneuver to clear away from Skylab. Mission Control would maneuver Skylab to the desired attitude orientation and fire the TRS to either boost it to a higher orbit or start a descent into the atmosphere.

Unfortunately, higher-than-expected solar activity heated Earth's atmosphere causing Skylab's orbit to decay more quickly than expected. Haise and Lousma had begun training for their Skylab rescue mission, however, the Shuttle's readiness for a planned first launch in 1979 was delayed due to technical problems, which would also delay their mission. Data showed that Skylab would reenter Earth's atmosphere in mid-1979, so NASA canceled the TRS activity and planned for a controlled descent for Skylab.

NASA Administrator Robert Frosch notified President Jimmy Carter that the planned rescue of Skylab was no longer possible and monitoring of Skylab ended. It will never be known how Skylab might have been utilized if the TRS reboost mission had taken place. It might have been refurbished and visited throughout the 1980s, with astronauts performing long-duration spaceflights long before the ISS was assembled and first occupied in November 2000.

* * *

What most people recall about Skylab is that it was the space station that crashed to Earth in July 1979. Most of the station burned up in the atmosphere, of course, but a few pieces, both large and small, survived reentry and landed on the western coast of Australia. NASA had done everything it could to direct it into the Indian Ocean and was mostly successful.

Luckily, because the western coast of Australia is sparsely populated, there was no property damage or injuries from the falling debris.

NASA was given a $400 ticket for littering by a local government in Australia. The ticket was issued in jest, in the hope that NASA would pay the fine as a gift to the Esperance Museum. NASA did not pay the fine, but many years later, a radio host in Barstow, California, convinced his listeners to cover the fine for NASA.

* * *

In 1977, four years after sewing the Skylab parasol, Mom was asked to work on another high-profile project for NASA while still employed by GE. In 1971, David Vetter, also known as the "Bubble Boy," was born in Houston with severe combined immunodeficiency disorder. He was confined to a plastic bubble to protect him from life-threatening infections. The bubble served as his protective shield against the outside world, was equipped with filtered air, temperature control, and allowed caregivers and family to safely interact with him.

When David was six years old, NASA developed a special suit that allowed him to go outside his bubble using an eight-foot-long cloth tube, as a tether, which enabled him to leave the bubble without risking contamination. He didn't want to wear the suit at first, but later became comfortable with it, using it seven times before outgrowing it.

NASA had also provided a second suit for him that he never used. Both spacesuits for David were sewn by my mother. One of the spacesuits is part of the Smithsonian's National Museum of American History collection.

* * *

In early 2017, my friend Dwight Steven-Boniecki, who lives in Germany and has written books about the Gemini and Skylab programs, informed me that he and his wife, Alexandra, were planning to produce and direct a full-length documentary about Skylab titled *Searching for Skylab: America's Forgotten Triumph*. My mother had passed away in 2007, and Dwight wanted to know if he could interview me for the film to tell Mom's story about her involvement with the parasol. Of course, I agreed.

Since I had been a high school classmate of Nan Kinzler, daughter of the NASA engineer who had developed the idea for the parasol, Jack Kinzler, I was able to arrange for Dwight to also interview Jack's widow, Sylvia, and one of Jack's sons, James, at the same time he interviewed me, at the Kinzlers' home (which is adjacent to Pete Conrad's former home) in Timber Cove.

The film premiered on February 8, 2018, at the U.S. Space and Rocket Center in Huntsville, Alabama, and has since won 29 awards at various film festivals around the world, including for Best Documentary, Best Director, Best Science Film, and Best Editing.

Several years ago, I became friends with another seamstress that supported NASA, Jean Wright, who worked on the Space Shuttle's Thermal Protection System at KSC, stitching protective coverings for the world's most sophisticated vehicle. Jean is one of eighteen women who sewed the thermal blankets that protected the Space Shuttle. She called the group "Sew Sisters." Jean considers Mom an honorary member of the "Sew Sisters," even though they never met.

Since the end of the Shuttle Program in 2011, Jean has remained involved with NASA as a docent at KSC, and also as a photographer, quilter, and speaker. She recently published a book titled *Sew Sister – The Untold Story of Jean Wright and NASA's Seamstresses.* Jean was kind enough to include the NASA photo of Mom sewing the Skylab parasol in her Author's Notes at the end of her book.

* * *

During the Skylab 50th anniversary celebration events in 2023, I was asked to moderate a panel at Space Center Houston titled "Skylab—What Did We Learn?" The panel included retired astronaut Story Musgrave (participating remotely); Dr. Helen Lane, a former NASA scientist and nutritionist; and former NASA Flight Director Bill Reeves.

Herb moderating the "Skylab-What Did We Learn" panel at Space Center Houston with panelists Story Musgrave (on screen), Dr. Helen Lane, and Bill Reeves

While there was much scientific knowledge gained about both the Sun and Earth from Skylab, the panel agreed that the most important lesson we learned from Skylab was that humans could live and work in space for extended periods. Skylab 4 Commander Jerry Carr agreed with that assessment. He put it this way, in his JSC Oral History Project interview in 2000:

"I think probably the most important contribution of the Skylab flight was the medical stuff. We proved, I think, just absolutely positively that the human being can live in weightless environment for an extended period of time, and it's, of course, subsequently been proved that you can stay up at least a year or a year and a half."

"But medically, we gathered the data that I think gave the Russians and other people the understanding and the courage to say, 'Okay, we can stay up for longer periods of time.' And I think that was a real breakthrough, because if you remember back in the Mercury days, the doctors weren't even sure if an astronaut could swallow or defecate or urinate on orbit. We have come a long, long way. Our experiments were very rigorous experiments. They were very well done, and data was very well taken. I think that that solved a lot of problems."

* * *

Herb with Skylab astronaut Joe Kerwin at Space Center Houston

Herb with Skylab/Shuttle astronaut Jack Lousma and his daughter, Mary, at Space Center Houston

* * *

Several months after the Space Center Houston event, I was invited by the Astronaut Scholarship Foundation to participate in a Skylab celebration event with Jack Lousma and Rusty Schweickart at the Kennedy Space Center Visitor Complex (KSCVC) on November 16, 2023—the 50th anniversary of the launch of the Skylab 4 crew. The main event was a screening of Dwight Steven-Boniecki's documentary film *Searching for Skylab* at the IMAX theater at KSCVC.

Before the film, Dwight moderated a panel of Jack, Rusty, and me to briefly discuss the Skylab Program. It was a great honor for me to speak on the same panel with those two legendary astronauts after having been the moderator of a panel with them a few years earlier.

The day started with an autograph and photo opportunity at the American Space Museum and Walk of Fame in Titusville that morning. After the panel and film screening at KSCVC that afternoon, we spent the evening at our hotel having drinks and dinner. I talked with Rusty about him being one of the founding members of the Association of Space Explorers, along with Loren Acton—who I was lucky enough to spend the day with at the Association of Space Explorers Congress in Houston in 2019.

Rusty was excited to talk about the Schweickart Prize for Planetary Defense he had recently established, aimed at improving our ability to protect life on Earth from the potential devastation of an asteroid. The prize will be awarded annually on June 30, International Asteroid Day.

L to R — "Searching for Skylab" documentary director Dwight Steven-Boniecki, Skylab/Shuttle astronaut Jack Lousma, Apollo 9 astronaut Rusty Schweickart, and Herb at the KSCVC IMAX Theater

11 - Apollo-Soyuz Test Project

The year after the Skylab 4 crew returned home, the Apollo–Soyuz Test Project (ASTP) was launched on July 15, 1975. It was the first crewed international space mission, a joint mission between the U.S. and the Soviet Union, and the first Soviet launch televised live. Unsurprisingly, the mission was referred to in the Soviet Union as Soyuz-Apollo. Millions of people watched on television as the Apollo spacecraft docked with the Soviet Soyuz capsule, symbolizing cooperation between the U.S. and the Soviet Union during the Cold War. It was the final flight of the Apollo spacecraft. After the launch, NASA began converting Launch Complex 39B and the Vehicle Assembly Building for use by the Space Shuttle Program.

During the mission, the three American astronauts—Tom Stafford (Commander), Vance Brand (Command Module Pilot), and Deke Slayton (Docking Module Pilot)—and two Soviet cosmonauts, Alexei Leonov and Valeri Kubasov, performed experiments both separately and jointly.

It would be the last crewed U.S. spaceflight for nearly six years, until STS-1 in 1981. It was also the last U.S. spaceflight in a capsule until Bob Behnken and Doug Hurley flew on the SpaceX Crew Dragon Demo-2 flight, forty-five years later, in 2020.

Both spacecraft launched on July 15 and docked together two days later. After docking, Stafford and Leonov shook hands through an open hatch. It was the first international handshake in space. Stafford and Leonov would become life-long friends.

For the next two days, the crews exchanged flags and gifts, shared meals, and took turns speaking each other's languages. Leonov said that Stafford, who was born and raised in Oklahoma, spoke with a drawl when speaking Russian. He joked that, in addition to English and Russian, "Oklahomski" was also spoken on the mission.

The ASTP mission was a success, but the Americans suffered a serious problem during their reentry and splashdown in the Pacific Ocean, near Hawaii. The crew was exposed to toxic fumes from the Command Module's Reaction Control System (RCS) thrusters. The fumes were drawn into the Command Module when the thrusters, which were supposed to have been shut down, began firing due to the motion of the Command Module under the parachutes.

The ASTP Medical Report (NASA SP-411) from 1977 states:

"While the spacecraft was still in an inverted position after landing, Stafford unstrapped and fell into the Command Module tunnel, hurting his right shoulder and elbow. He unstowed the oxygen masks and gave them to his crewmembers. Not until the spacecraft turned upright, approximately 3½ minutes later, did Stafford notice that Brand's mask was hanging on the side of his face and that he was unconscious. According to available history, it appears that Brand was unconscious for approximately 50 seconds. Brand recovered quickly when his face mask was positioned properly and the oxygen flow was increased."

"Once in an upright position, the postlanding ventilation was activated, the flotation gear was positioned, and the CM hatch was opened. This further improved the ventilation and removal of toxic gases from the cabin."

* * *

While still working for GE, making soft goods for NASA, my mother made the cloth ASTP gift bag that was carried aboard the Command Module and presented to the Soviet crew. The gift bag carried items such as the U.S. half of the sectionized ASTP Commemorative Plaque (which was matched with the Soviet half in orbit), ten 8x12 inch American flags, ten 8x16 inch Soviet flags, a box of white spruce tree seeds, and the ASTP Certification to authorize the docking. Mom made two gift bags, one to be presented to the Soviets and another for the Smithsonian Institution.

* * *

A few years ago, I heard Tom Stafford speak at an event held at Space Center Houston. A young boy asked him, "When you were my age, did you want to be an astronaut?" Stafford, who was 88 at the time, replied, "Son, when I was your age, there was no such thing as an astronaut." Stafford recently passed away at the age of 93.

12 - Starting Out at NASA

I hate to admit that I didn't have a strong desire to become an astronaut growing up. I studied business at the University of Texas, never dreaming of a future career at NASA. I assumed everyone who worked at NASA was a scientist, an engineer, a doctor, or an astronaut.

While it's true that the majority of NASA employees fit into those categories, about one-third fill other supporting roles in careers such as contracting, law, finance, human resources, public affairs, information technology, and facility management. There are also many NASA employees working in fields that didn't exist at NASA when I started in the mid-1970s, such as social media.

While at UT, I had a part-time job at the IRS Regional Service Center in Austin to help pay my way through school. My job title was Tax Examiner, which meant I would review the Federal Income Tax returns submitted by individuals to make sure that all of the required information (e.g., name, address, Social Security number) had been provided, that all of the necessary forms (e.g., Schedule A, Schedule B, W-2) were attached and stapled together in the correct order, and that the return was signed.

This was many years before electronic forms were accepted by the IRS, so every return was a paper form that was almost always completed using a pen or pencil. A few forms were completed with a typewriter, but that was rare. Our performance evaluations were based on a combination of how many returns we processed and how many errors we made.

Each Tax Examiner group had a Reviewer who reviewed the work of that group's Tax Examiners, counting how many returns we processed and how many errors we made (e.g., not noticing that information or a form was missing). After a few months, my error rate was so low that I was promoted to the position of Reviewer for my group. I enjoyed that position much more.

In January 1975, at the start of my final semester at UT, I had no firm plans for what I would do or where I would work after graduating. During that time, I heard my co-workers at the IRS talking about a test called the Professional and Administrative Career Examination (PACE).

Our jobs were considered clerical and did not pay well. I was working part-time and had no intention of making a career at the IRS, but some of my co-workers were working full-time and were hoping to be promoted to a professional position within the Government. In those days, the most common way to get a job, or be promoted, with the Federal Government, was to take a Civil Service exam and hope you scored well enough to be offered a job or a promotion.

The PACE exam graded you in six skill categories (e.g., verbal comprehension, deductive reasoning) on a scale from 70 to 100. If you scored below a 70 in any category, you failed that part of the test and were not given a score. When registering for the test, you could indicate on the application which cities with Government agencies you would prefer to work in, if offered a job. I listed Houston as a preferred location without it occurring to me that NASA was one of the Federal agencies in Houston.

I took the PACE exam in February 1975, and in March, I received a letter from the U.S. Civil Service Commission with my scores. To my surprise, I had scored 100 in four of the six categories and scored 98 in the other two. An even greater surprise came a few weeks later when I received a letter from NASA asking if I would be interested in coming to Houston for a job interview. That was an easy decision! To this day, that series of events seems surreal to me.

I've often wondered how my life might have been different if I hadn't taken that part-time job with the IRS and hadn't become aware of the PACE exam. The thought of a career in the Government had never occurred to me until I overheard my IRS co-workers talking about that exam. I had assumed I'd find a job somewhere in the corporate world/private industry after leaving school.

One more bit of luck came my way when I showed up at JSC for my job interview. I learned that the person interviewing me, J. P. Harris, the deputy director of the JSC Procurement Office, was the father of one of my high school friends, Ron Harris. I don't know if that connection helped with the interview, but I'm certain it didn't hurt. That same day, I was offered a job with NASA as a contract specialist at an annual salary of $9,303.

* * *

The Johnson Space Center was originally named the Manned Spacecraft Center when it officially opened in September 1963. The name was changed to the Johnson Space Center in 1973 in honor of the late U.S. president and Texas native, Lyndon B. Johnson.

Most of the land on which JSC sits was sold to the Government by Rice University in September 1962 for $10. NASA purchased an additional 600 acres for $10 so the property would face a highway. I've often heard a myth that Rice still owns the land and leases it to NASA and that the JSC facility is built in a campus style in case the university might use the land again at some point in the future. That is not true.

Because I had been on-site at JSC many times, I felt at home when I reported for work on my first day, even though it was a bit intimidating to think that I was freshly out of college and suddenly working with some of the most brilliant and accomplished people in the world.

These same people had been responsible, in the recent past, for landing 12 men on the Moon, miraculously saving the Apollo 13 crew, sending 3 Skylab crews to orbit, setting a record for the length of time humans had spent in space (84 days), and were now working on the design of the Space Shuttle and developing new spacesuits.

Growing up just a few miles from JSC and working on-site with the news media between 1969 and 1973 also helped me feel comfortable there. It was awkward, however, when I recognized the parent of a high school friend who was now a co-worker. It was always nice to see a familiar face, but it took me a while to become comfortable addressing them by their first names when I had always addressed them more formally as Mr. or Mrs.

My job as a contract specialist in the procurement office was to acquire supplies, equipment, and services for NASA. That was almost always accomplished through competing, negotiating, awarding, and administering a government contract. Sometimes, when the supply or service we were buying had a low dollar value, we could accomplish this by awarding a simple Purchase Order, which was quicker, easier, and involved far less paperwork than a formal contract.

I spent my first two years at NASA taking numerous training courses to learn about the massive number of laws and regulations governing government contracts. At the time, there were no college courses covering that subject, so we primarily learned through on-the-job training. For the first year or so, I rotated between different procurement offices to get a feel for the whole organization, spending approximately three months in each office. Some offices supported the Programs (e.g., Space Shuttle), some supported other technical organizations (e.g., mission operations, engineering, space and life sciences), and some supported institutional offices (e.g., logistics, data management, security).

In early 1978, I was assigned to the Research and Technology Branch to work on the Extravehicular Mobility Unit (EMU) contract that NASA had awarded to Hamilton Standard in 1974 to design and build new spacesuits for the upcoming Space Shuttle flights. The contract required Hamilton Standard, located in Windsor Locks, CT, to design and build 18 EMU spacesuits.

The expected lifespan of the spacesuits was 15 years. The value of the contract was at least $300 million in 1975 dollars (around $3 billion today). ILC (International Latex Corporation) Dover, better known for making women's bras and girdles before becoming involved in making the Apollo spacesuits, was a major subcontractor. Since it was my first experience with a major NASA contract, I was working under the guidance of a senior contracting officer (CO), Tommy McPhillips, who became a close friend.

* * *

I can thank Tommy for my interest in live theater. While we were working together in 1979, his wife was performing in the chorus of a production of *Hello, Dolly!* at College of the Mainland Community Theatre in Texas City, TX. He wanted to see the show but didn't want to go alone so he asked if I would go with him. I agreed to go and that day changed my life.

I had never had a serious interest in theater or performing as an actor. I wasn't even in my high school senior class play, *Mame*. I was the band president my senior year of high school so, naturally, I chose to be in the orchestra for the show rather than performing on stage with most of my fellow seniors.

Watching that performance of *Hello, Dolly*, in that intimate theater, where you could almost reach out and touch the actors on stage if you were in the front row, hooked me on live theater for life. After the performance that evening, I asked someone how I could become involved.

I told them I had no acting experience but that I had lots of experience playing trombone, including five years in the University of Texas Longhorn Band. They told me that there was an upcoming production of *Jesus Christ Superstar* at the theater and suggested that I audition for the orchestra.

I took that advice and was accepted into the orchestra. A few months after *Jesus Christ Superstar*, I also played in the orchestra for a production of *The Sound of Music* at the same theater. After being involved in those two shows, I was even more determined to stay involved in live theater. I was single, so I had plenty of time on my hands for the auditions, rehearsals, performances, and learning lines required to perform on stage. Later that season, I auditioned for a role in the chorus of the musical *Kismet* and was accepted.

I performed in another 15 shows at different theaters over the next four years in the local area, including musicals (*Pippin, Fiddler on the Roof, Annie,* and *Mame*), comedies (*Arsenic and Old Lace* and *Footlight Frenzy*), Shakespeare (*Othello, The Comedy of*

Errors, The Taming of the Shrew, and *A Midsummer Night's Dream*), and a murder mystery (*The Mousetrap*). I also served as a stage manager, operated a spotlight, and ran the sound equipment for a few shows in which I didn't appear on stage.

Several years later, in early 1985, I accepted a one-year special assignment at NASA Headquarters in Washington, D.C. That move from the area, along with getting married and becoming a father a few years later, led me to put my acting career on hold.

The next time I performed on stage was 33 years later, in 2018, when I played Kris Kringle in a production of *Miracle on 34th Street* at the Clear Creek Community Theatre (CCCT), which was across the street from the Johnson Space Center in Nassau Bay. Since then, I've performed in four more shows at CCCT, and I've been on its Board of Directors since 2020.

* * *

My first government travel experience was to attend a meeting at the Hamilton Standard facility in Windsor Locks, CT, to discuss the EMU contract. I was the junior member of the group traveling with Tommy McPhillips and two or three senior NASA spacesuit engineers.

I had not done a lot of traveling outside Texas at that point in my life. I will not forget that first evening when, after going out to dinner with my co-workers, one of them said, "Hey, let's drive up to Springfield, Massachusetts, and watch some Jai alai games."

I thought about it briefly and said, "Wait a minute. You want to drive to another state? Would you drop me off at the hotel first?" My co-worker replied, "Don't worry. It's only a 30-minute drive." I replied, "Are you kidding? You can drive to another state in 30 minutes?" So I went along and, having never seen Jai alai before, had a great time.

* * *

That EMU contract has turned out to be a huge success. Hamilton Standard would deliver 18 EMU spacesuits for the Space Shuttle Program. Today, those suits are over 40 years old and have been used in over 200 spacewalks. Of those 18 suits delivered, suit #1 was used only for certification, suit #2 was destroyed during ground testing in 1980, two suits were lost in the *Challenger* accident in 1986, and two additional suits were lost in the *Columbia* accident in 2003.

Another suit was lost in the SpaceX CRS-7 cargo resupply mission mishap in 2015. Seven of the suits are in various states of refurbishment and maintenance. The remaining four suits are still in use on the ISS forty years after they were delivered.

NASA recently contracted with Axiom Space to develop and deliver next-generation spacesuits (AxEMU) for the Artemis Moon landing missions. NASA's recent Exploration Extravehicular Mobility Unit (xEMU) development efforts will serve as the basis for the design and development of the AxEMU.

* * *

One of the NASA engineers I worked with on the EMU contract in the 1970s was Joe Kosmo, who had worked on the design, development, and testing of Mercury, Gemini, Apollo, and Skylab spacesuits prior to his work on the Shuttle EMU spacesuits. Joe knew nothing about spacesuits when he started working for NASA in 1961, but neither did anyone else.

Joe retired in 2011 after a 50-year career with NASA. After I left the EMU Program in 1979 to work in the Shuttle

Program, I didn't see Joe again for 40 years until I also retired and was elected to the Board of Directors of the NASA Alumni League, where he was a director. It has been a pleasure to reconnect and reminisce with him about those early days being involved with the Shuttle spacesuits.

* * *

In January 1978, NASA announced the selection of Astronaut Group 8. It was the first group of new astronauts since 1969 and was notable for being the first to include women and minorities. There were six women, three African Americans, and an Asian American in the group. It was also the largest class selected at that time. Astronaut Group 16, a group of 44 selected in 1996, is the only larger group.

With Group 8, NASA stopped appointing astronauts upon their selection. Instead, new selections are considered astronaut candidates (or AsCans), until they complete 2 years of training. Group 8 is referred to as the Thirty-Five New Guys, or TFNG. However, within the group, it was known to stand for the military phrase, "The F*cking New Guys," used to signify newcomers to a group. The tradition of assigning a nickname to each class by the previous class started with Group 8 and has continued since, with one exception—Astronaut Group 11, selected in 1985.

* * *

The Shuttle Approach and Landing Test (ALT) program was a sequence of 16 crewed and uncrewed runway and flight tests in 1977 of the Shuttle *Enterprise* to test its flight characteristics—11 flights while mated to the Shuttle Carrier Aircraft and five free flights with a crew. The Approach and Landing tests were flown by two-man crews. The first crew was Commander Fred Haise and Pilot Gordon Fullerton and the second crew was Commander Joe Engle and Pilot Dick Truly.

The tests were conducted at the Dryden Flight Research Center (renamed the Armstrong Flight Research Center in 2014) at Edwards Air Force Base in California. The location offers dry conditions, few rainy days per year, and large, flat open spaces with a runway length of over 40,000 feet.

The 1ˢᵗ ALT crew – Commander Fred Haise (L) and Pilot Gordon Fullerton (R) [NASA photo]

On Friday, March 10, 1978, a few months after the Shuttle Approach and Landing Test program was completed with Shuttle *Enterprise*, it had a layover at Ellington Field on its way from Edwards Air Force Base, carried atop the Boeing 747, to Marshall Space Flight Center. There, *Enterprise* was mated with an external fuel tank and rocket boosters for vertical ground vibration tests.

I was one of approximately 240,000 visitors who saw *Enterprise* at Ellington over that weekend. JSC Director Chris Kraft and Deke Slayton spoke to the crowd at a short ceremony on Friday. Slayton received the NASA Outstanding Leadership

Medal, and the Shuttle project managers and the crew of the 747 received NASA's Exceptional Service Medal.

Deke Slayton presenting NASA Outstanding Leadership Medals at Ellington [NASA photo]

Fifteen other key NASA personnel, including astronauts and 747 crew members, were presented NASA Exceptional Service Medals for their role in ALT, including Fred Haise, Gordon Fullerton, Joe Engle, Dick Truly, Carl Peterson, Tom McElmurry, Louis Guidry, John Kiker, and Don Puddy.

* * *

On the subject of the Approach and Landing Tests, have you ever wondered who came up with the seemingly crazy idea to fly the Shuttle attached to the top of a 747?

John Kiker was one of the original engineers with NASA's Space Task Group who moved to Houston when the Manned Spacecraft Center opened. He was Chief of the Mechanisms Branch at JSC when the Shuttle Program began.

NASA's original plan for returning the Shuttles to KSC was to load fuel into their cargo bay, attach jet engines under their wings, and fly them like airplanes back to KSC. Loading a large container of fuel into the Shuttle's payload bay would require running fuel lines through the wings to the engines. It also would have required the removal of tiles on the underside of the wings and required reinforcement of the wings.

Kiker, who was a radio-controlled model airplane enthusiast, started to think "outside the box." He came up with the idea of putting the Shuttle on top of a Boeing 747. NASA was not sold on the idea initially, thinking it wouldn't work.

To prove that the two vehicles could fly together in this formation and separate in flight as well, he built 1/40-scale radio-controlled models of both the Shuttle and a 747. His models proved that it was a feasible concept and convinced NASA management that it would work. The ability to separate in flight allowed NASA to conduct those Approach and Landing tests.

Sitting on top of the newly-named Shuttle Carrier Aircraft or SCA, Shuttle *Enterprise* taxied out to the Edwards AFB runway on February 18, 1977. With a large crowd looking on, the two aircraft took off, landed, and made history that day.

The Shuttles most frequently landed at the Shuttle Landing Facility in Florida, but they also landed 54 times in California and once in New Mexico. In those instances, the SCA was needed to ferry the Shuttles back to KSC.

Space Center Houston has an exhibit featuring the Shuttle mockup *Independence* sitting atop one of NASA's two Shuttle Carrier Aircraft. Visitors are allowed to step inside both the *Independence* mockup and the SCA, which includes a tribute to John Kiker.

The Shuttle Independence mockup sitting atop one of the Shuttle Carrier Aircraft at Space Center Houston

* * *

When I recall this story, my first thought is, "If they can carry a Space Shuttle on top of a passenger plane with no problem, I call BS on overweight baggage fees!"

13 - Buying Shuttle Orbiter Vehicles

In July 1979, I was assigned to the Shuttle Orbiter Procurement Section, where I would work for the next five years. This was less than two years before the first Shuttle flight, STS-1, in April 1981. The contract for development, production, and delivery of the Space Shuttle Orbiter vehicles had been awarded to North American Rockwell in July 1972 with an initial value of $2.6 billion. Rockwell had also built the Command and Service Modules for the Apollo Program.

Separate contracts would be awarded for other Shuttle elements: the main engines (Rocketdyne), the solid rocket boosters (Thiokol Corp.), and the external tank (Martin Marietta). Those three contracts would be managed at the Marshall Space Flight Center (MSFC) in Huntsville, AL, which was responsible for propulsion elements.

Unlike most of the previous contracts I had been involved with, which were administered by a single contracting officer with assistance from a single contract specialist, this critical, multi-billion-dollar Shuttle Orbiter Vehicle contract, designated with the contract number NAS9-14000, had at least 8 to 10 contracting officers and contract specialists administering it.

The contract was so large and complex that it was divided into multiple segments called Schedules. Schedule A covered the initial Design, Development, Test, and Evaluation (known as DDT&E) phase; Schedule B covered the Production phase (the construction of the Orbiter vehicles); Schedule C covered Payload Integration; Schedule D covered Systems Integration; and Schedule E covered Operations Support.

Shuttle Orbiter Vehicle in early stages of being assembled at the Rockwell plant in Palmdale, CA [NASA photo]

When I was assigned to help administer this contract in July 1979, Shuttle *Enterprise*, used in the Approach and Landing Tests, had been delivered. The *Columbia* Orbiter had also been delivered just four months earlier, in March 1979. The Orbiter vehicle DDT&E phase had been completed and the Production phase was underway. I was assigned to help manage Schedules C (Payload Integration) and D (Systems Integration).

Even though *Columbia* had already been delivered, there were still hundreds of design changes and improvements that seemed to be constantly happening to the Orbiter vehicles in the queue, *Challenger*, *Discovery*, and *Atlantis*. In fact, that was our biggest challenge—trying to keep up contractually with all the changes that were being made. Whenever a NASA Contract Change Board (CCB) approved a change to the requirements, our office prepared and issued a Contract Change Authorization (CCA) to Rockwell that specified the change to be made to the vehicle(s).

Rockwell then had to respond to our office with proposed cost and schedule impacts. When the Rockwell proposal was received, our office requested a technical evaluation of the proposal from the engineer that had requested/approved the change. When we received the technical evaluation, which included comments and recommendations regarding the proposed cost and schedule impacts, we formulated a negotiation position that typically included a target cost as well as a minimum and maximum cost range. This negotiation position then had to be approved at least one level above us, depending on the dollar value of the change.

Once that position was approved, we entered into negotiations with a Rockwell representative and, hopefully, reached an agreement. Next, we prepared a supplemental agreement that documented all changes to be made to the contract, including cost and schedule impacts, as well as changes to the Statement of Work (a detailed description of the work to be done) and any other changes to the terms and conditions of the contract. Once the supplemental agreement was signed by both Rockwell and NASA, the changes to the contract had to be reviewed by NASA's legal counsel to ensure legal sufficiency.

As you might presume, this process did not happen quickly or easily. I recall the Shuttle contract having 200-300 outstanding changes at any given time that had been issued but had not yet made it completely through the proposal/evaluation/negotiation/agreement/review/signature process. We were drowning in changes and falling so far behind in the process that we were having to make special arrangements contractually so that we could legally make payments to Rockwell for work already completed.

In Government contracting, you cannot pay a contractor more than the dollar value of the contract. It makes sense, right? Our problem was that we could not increase the value of the contract until the change process had been completed and definitized. We were so far behind that Rockwell was completing the work and billing us before the negotiated value could be added to the contract. We had to obtain approval to provisionally increase the contract value so that we could continue making payments.

I recall one particular action I was assigned to complete. I was given a list of 31 CCAs to definitize, for which we had received 31 proposals. Rather than go through the whole process 31 different times, I reached an agreement with Rockwell to bundle all of the changes into one comprehensive action. I suggested to Rockwell, "We can discuss the cost impacts of each of these 31 changes individually, but instead of agreeing to a dollar amount for each one, let's reach an agreement on the total bottom-line value." So, instead of 31 negotiations, we only had to do one. For documentation purposes, you can spread the total dollars however you want among the individual 31 changes, and I'll spread the dollars however I want for my purposes."

Since that approach also made the process easier for the Rockwell team, they agreed—and it worked. Getting one supplemental agreement approved, with a total value of around $1 million, was much faster and easier than getting 31 approved individually.

* * *

In late 1983, I led a $150 million negotiation with Rockwell to make changes to the Systems Integration Schedule of the Shuttle contract. The change was fairly complex: extending the period of performance by two years, converting the contract type from level-of-effort (in which the contractor is required only to provide a specified number of labor hours) to completion form (in which the contractor must complete a specified product or service), and adding a cost incentive to the contract's fee structure. There were five of us on my JSC negotiation team, which included two budget analysts. Rockwell's negotiation team was led by Jeaniel Hill, one of Rockwell's senior contract managers. Jeaniel was a brilliant woman and a tough negotiator, with whom I would become life-long friends.

We had begun in-person negotiations at JSC on December 12 and by Friday, December 16, had made little progress. With the weekend and Christmas holidays approaching, the Rockwell team informed me that they planned to return home to California and return the following week to continue negotiations. I informed my branch chief, Gene Easley, of their plans. Unhappy with that approach, he called the Rockwell team's manager in Downey, CA, and insisted that their team remain in Houston and continue negotiations through the weekend.

Our teams got back together to continue negotiations that afternoon. Jeaniel was not happy with the thought of having to work through the weekend in Houston rather than going home, as she had planned. Our teams were sitting at a long table in a conference room when she took her hotel room key (this was before hotels started using magnetic cards for door keys) out of her purse and proclaimed, "If I have to spend the weekend here, someone is coming to my room!" She then slung her hotel room key across the table toward our team, and it came to a stop directly in front of one of our budget analysts, Dale Swanson. His face turned as white as a ghost. Luckily for Dale, she was kidding (I think).

* * *

During this time, while my head was buried in the contractual work, the Shuttle Program was experiencing multiple technical delays. The biggest problem was the thermal protection system tiles falling off. All of the Orbiters, including *Columbia*, were built in Palmdale, CA, about 60 miles north of Los Angeles. After *Columbia* was built, it was flown to Florida. When it took off atop the Shuttle Carrier Aircraft from Palmdale in 1979, tiles fell off as they went down the runway. The tiles were falling off even before they were off the ground.

That led to the requirement for a better understanding of how the tiles were attached so that they would remain in place more reliably. The problem took two years to solve. There were also problems with *Columbia's* computers and software for the avionics that were taking longer than expected to solve. Rather than launching for the first time in 1979 as initially planned, these problems contributed to a two-year schedule delay that pushed STS-1 to 1981.

One morning in March 1981, I walked into an elevator in Building 1 at JSC and spotted a calendar taped to the wall. In addition to some frustration from all the delays in the Shuttle Program at that time, there was much anticipation and excitement. We knew that we were getting close to the launch of STS-1. The calendar in the elevator, obviously created by a Rockwell employee, was captioned, "Rockwell March is On! STS-1 We WILL Launch in March."

When you looked closely at the 12 months shown on the calendar, they were labeled: "January, February, March, March, March, March, March, March…December." I pulled the calendar off the elevator wall to save as a souvenir. I still have that calendar.

Of course, we did not launch in March. STS-1 finally launched on April 12, 1981. John Young was the commander, and Bob "Crip" Crippen was the pilot for that first Shuttle Flight on *Columbia*. It was the first test flight of a new American spacecraft to carry a crew.

Young and Crippen had been assigned to the STS-1 crew in March 1979. You might think that, given the dangers of flying a vehicle that had never been to orbit before, NASA had to "twist some arms" to find two astronauts willing to ride it for the first time. The opposite was true. I learned that every astronaut in the corps would have been honored and thrilled to be assigned to that mission.

After the launch, Crippen said, "My biggest worry was—would we launch? There were so many things that could go wrong with the vehicle. It was pretty complicated and I could see us going through several scrubs, but we only went through one. I was pleasantly surprised when we did lift off." John Young had said of that experience, "If they were going to light off seven million pounds of thrust under you and you weren't a little bit excited, you didn't understand the situation."

There is a John Young story in which he acknowledges the risk he would be taking. Astronaut Joe Allen was assigned as support crew to STS-1 and also served as the reentry Capcom for that mission. Allen also drove Young and Crippen to Ellington Airport, from where they would fly from Houston to the Kennedy Space Center for the launch.

Allen tells this story (excerpted from his interview for the JSC Oral History Project) about John Young: "When we got ready to fly STS-1, I was support crew to Young and Crippen, and I was also an assistant to (JSC Director) George Abbey. I was the 'Bubba.' George said, 'Joe, we're going to go take John and Crip out to the airplanes. Come with me.' I said, 'Fine. Why do you need me?' He said, 'My car won't start.' I said, 'Oh, terrific.' He couldn't get his car started. I said, 'Okay,' then we went down and got in my car. I'd had lunch with them the day before, and John hadn't had any money, so I'd bought his lunch for him."

On their way to Ellington in the car, Young tried to repay his lunch debt from the previous day but Allen refused at first. Young insisted, "You don't go fly these things when you've got debts." Allen accepted the money so that all of Young's debts were paid before launch.

Coincidentally, STS-1 launched on the 20th anniversary of the first human spaceflight by Yuri Gagarin for the Soviet Union. The launch had been scheduled for two days earlier, but was delayed due to a technical problem.

The main objective of STS-1 was to make it to orbit and return safely to Earth. The crew spent most of their time in orbit (53 hours) conducting tests of the Orbiter's systems. All flight test objectives were accomplished successfully.

During the ride into space, Young's heart rate did not go above 90 beats per minute, while first-time flyer Crippen's heart rate rose to nearly 130 beats per minute. Young joked afterwards that he was too old for his heart to beat any faster. Flight Director Neil Hutchinson mused, "Young must have been asleep the whole time."

NASA believed that the external tanks, which were filled with super-cooled liquid hydrogen and liquid oxygen, should be painted white to help protect them from the ultraviolet light of the Sun during the time they spent on the launch pad.

Space Shuttle model gift to Herb from Rockwell International

Martin Marietta, which built the ETs and is now part of Lockheed Martin, left the rust-colored spray-on insulation unpainted beginning with STS-3, saving approximately 600 pounds of weight. After the successful STS-1 flight, Rockwell presented me with a Shuttle model as a gift (which I was allowed to accept since its value was below $20) for my work with them. I love that the external tank on the model is white.

Another Shuttle memento I received is a small ½ inch cube of a segment of a thermal tile, embedded in Lucite, which flew on the STS-1 flight. The reverse side of the piece reads, "This is a segment of thermal tile which protected the Space Shuttle Orbiter *Columbia* from the heat of reentry on its first flight, April 12-14, 1981."

* * *

After the last "test" flight, STS-4, the Space Shuttle was declared operational. During the STS-4 launch one week earlier, the solid rocket boosters (SRBs) had been lost when their main parachutes failed, causing the empty casings to hit the ocean at high velocity and sink. The only other mission in which the SRBs were not recovered was the STS-51-L launch of *Challenger*.

* * *

I received a copy of the "Performance Summary" document prepared by Rockwell for the STS-1 flight shortly after its completion. The document describes the numerous tests and objectives successfully completed during the flight. Reading the document again 40 years later, one section stands out, describing the performance of the Thermal Protection System. The document states, "A total of 303 tile impacts (either surface coating chips or gouges) were noted. The majority were identified as having occurred during ascent."

"Most are readily repairable during turnaround operations. Impact strikes on the upper forward RCS (Reaction Control System) and window canopy show that debris from the ET was passing over the top of the Orbiter. Impacts noted on the forward OMS (Orbital Maneuvering System) pod tiles indicate that debris strikes may have dislodged or cracked some OMS tiles and contributed to the loss of the tiles observed missing during orbital operations. All other tiles are accounted for."

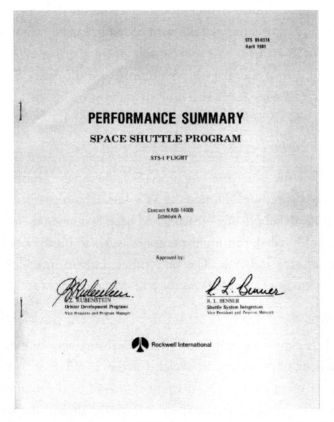

Performance Summary for STS-1 flight prepared by Rockwell for NASA

The report seems to downplay the problem of debris striking the Orbiter's Thermal Protection System on launch. We know now that this problem would haunt the Shuttle Program for most of its life.

* * *

Soon after starting my career at NASA, I joined the Space City-Houston Chapter of the National Contract Management Association (NCMA). I was an active member and, in 1982, served as Chair of the Programs Committee. (I would later be elected vice president for the 2000-2001 Chapter year and president for the 2001-2002 Chapter year.) As Chair of the Programs Committee, it was my responsibility to arrange the time, place, subject, and guest speaker for each of our monthly meetings.

In the Fall of 1982, Patricia "Patty" Cobb, the chair of the Programs Committee for the Houston Chapter of the American Society for Public Administration (ASPA), contacted me about the possibility of our two organizations holding a joint meeting.

The ASPA wanted to present its Distinguished Public Servant Award to Dr. Chris Kraft, NASA's first Flight Director, who was in his tenth year as the director of MSC/JSC. Patty asked me to take the lead in arranging a guest speaker to present the award to Dr. Kraft at a jointly planned dinner meeting.

Wanting someone of equal or near-equal status to Kraft to present the award to Dr. Kraft, I first contacted John Glenn, who at the time was a U.S. Senator from Ohio. Senator Glenn replied with a letter expressing his regret that he would be unable to attend, stating that "the press of legislative business coupled with long Senate sessions prevented [him] from attending many of the events to which he was invited."

My second choice was Alan Shepard, the first American in space, who I had met 10 years earlier while working for the news media covering the Apollo missions. Shepard had retired from NASA, but he still lived in the local area. At the time, he was president of the Windward Company, a Texas distributor for Coors beer. I called him and he told me that he would be honored to make the presentation to Dr. Kraft.

United States Senate

WASHINGTON, D.C. 20510

November 29, 1982

Mr. Herb Baker
PO Box 961
League City, Texas 77573

Dear Mr. Baker:

I am sorry that I was unable to attend the joint ALPA and NCMA dinner that honored Dr. Christopher C. Kraft, at the Meridien Hotel in Houston, Texas on November 19, 1982.

The press of legislative business coupled with long Senate sessions prevented me from attending many of the events to which I was invited.

Again, thank you for your kind invitation and if there is ever a time that I, or my staff, can be of assistance please do not hesitate to contact us.

Best regards.

Sincerely,

John Glenn
United States Senator

JG/cbd

Letter from John Glenn declining my invitation to present the Distinguished Public Service Award to Chris Kraft

Alan Shepard presenting the Distinguished Public Servant award to Chris Kraft

Herb at head table (at far right) as Dr. Kraft accepts the Distinguished Public Servant Award presented by ASPA and NCMA

The dinner and award presentation at the Meridien Hotel in downtown Houston, on November 19, 1982, was a success. The "icing on the cake" for me was that after staying late to take care of business with the hotel, I saw Dr. Kraft and Shepard sitting together in the hotel bar having a drink, so I joined them for a few minutes. While I was with them, I got

Dr. Kraft to autograph my copy of the program for that evening. When I mentioned this to friends, some asked why I didn't also get Shepard's autograph. It had not occurred to me to ask Shepard to also sign my program. I now wish I had.

BAKER

The Distinguished
Public Servant Award

1982

presented by
The American Society for Public Administration
and
The National Contract Management Association

Herb's program for the Kraft award dinner signed by Chris Kraft

* * *

Kraft retired as center director a few months later and, in 2011, Building 30 at JSC was renamed the Christopher C. Kraft, Jr. Mission Control Center. Gerry Griffin replaced Dr. Kraft as JSC center director when Kraft retired in 1982.

Kraft was quoted as saying that he never wanted to be an astronaut, adding, "I liked my job better than theirs. I got to go on every flight, and besides that, I got to tell them what to do."

The Christopher C. Kraft, Jr., Mission Control Center at JSC

* * *

Herb celebrating his 30th birthday in his office in Bldg. 1 at JSC

One of the few NASA-related photos I have of myself during this period was a shot taken on my 30th birthday. I had a desk on the third floor of Building 1, with a window seat overlooking the inner campus of JSC. It gave me a great view of Building 4 South, where the astronaut offices are located, and Building 7, where the Crew Systems Laboratory is located.

My officemates decorated my desk that day. (Note the 1980s-era telephone and desktop calculator on my desk.)

* * *

As JSC center director, Gerry Griffin changed the Shuttle mission designations from the original system (e.g., STS-1, STS-2) to a new system, assigning a number to indicate the planned year of the launch, the launch site (there had been plans to launch some flights from Vandenberg Air Force Base, which never materialized), and a letter to indicate the planned order of the launch for that year.

For example, the mission that would have been designated STS-10 was now called Mission 41-B (*4* for fiscal year 1984, *1* for the KSC launch site, and *B* for the second launch that fiscal year). Gerry Griffin had been one of the Flight Directors for Apollo 13. It is believed that the reason for the Shuttle mission designation change was that Griffin did not want an STS-13.

The STS-41-B mission, the first flight using the new mission numbering system, flew in early February 1984. That mission was also notable for a couple of other reasons. It was the first landing at KSC's Shuttle Landing Facility after eight landings at Edwards Air Force Base and one at the White Sands Missile Range (STS-3).

It was also the mission during which Bruce McCandless took the first untethered spacewalk with the Manned Maneuvering Unit (MMU). McCandless went as far as 322 feet from the Orbiter.

Astronaut Bruce McCandless II performing the 1ˢᵗ untethered spacewalk with the MMU [NASA photo – taken by Hoot Gibson on STS-41-B]

McCandless was photographed on his spacewalk by crewmate Hoot Gibson through the window of the Shuttle *Challenger.* Later in the flight, Bob Stewart also flew the MMU. Their crewmates gave McCandless and Stewart the nicknames Buck Rogers and Flash Gordon. The photo of McCandless floating freely above Earth's horizon against the black sky is one of my favorite NASA photos.

* * *

In February 1984, I was promoted to a supervisory role in the Center Operations Procurement Office. The NAS9-14000 Space Shuttle contract I had been working on for five years did not end until it was absorbed into a new Space Flight Operations Contract (SFOC) twelve years later, in 1996, twenty-four years after it was awarded in 1972. By that time, its value had increased to more than $16 billion.

14 - Center Operations

During his January 1984 State of the Union address, President Reagan directed NASA to develop a permanently inhabited space station. The Program, called Space Station Freedom, was never completed and, after multiple redesigns and budget cuts, the project became the International Space Station Program around 1993. I eventually spent four years working on the Space Station Freedom Program (1985-1988) before it evolved into the ISS, and later spent another six years working in the ISS Program (from 1996-1999 and again from 2004-2007).

However, my new position in 1984 was supporting JSC Center Operations. As part of that new job, I received a contracting officer (CO) warrant, which is a level above the contract specialist position. Being a first-time supervisor, as well as a new contracting officer, meant an increase in responsibility, but it was one I was excited to take on.

Contracting officers, the only people authorized to bind the federal government to a contract, have a fair amount of power. The contracting officer warrant allows them to negotiate on behalf of the U.S. Government and, as the government's agent, only CO's may execute, modify, or terminate a contract. Not even a NASA center director or NASA administrator has that authority.

After buying Shuttle Orbiter vehicles for five years, the move to supporting center operations was a big change. In this office, we primarily processed small purchases (simplified acquisitions valued at less than $3,000) and awarded contracts for equipment and routine institutional support services, such as security, IT, logistics, and building maintenance.

The group of contract specialists that I supervised was small, just seven people, but at least three of them were outstanding contracting professionals who had long, successful careers with NASA—Robbie LaBrier, Larry Kenyon, and Ginger Darnell. We have become lifelong friends since we first worked together 40 years ago.

I spent just one year in this position before moving on to my next role, but it was an exciting year for me because 1984 was the year NASA began using desktop computers. It took a while for desktop computers to be widely distributed among all employees. Initially, only supervisors received computers. The timing was perfect for me, of course, since I had just become a supervisor. Microsoft Windows 2.0, the first full Windows operating system, was not released until three years later, in December 1987, so our first computers used an operating system called DOS (Disk Operating System) which had very limited functionality, compared to later versions of Microsoft Windows.

The programs (or apps) loaded on our computers were a word processor (PFS:Write and later WordPerfect), a spreadsheet program (Lotus1-2-3), and a graphics program (Harvard Graphics). With DOS, you could use only one of those programs at a time. If you were using the word processor and wanted to switch to the spreadsheet program, you had to exit the word processor, return to the Main Menu, and then open the spreadsheet program from there.

We had a very basic IBM email system called PROFS (for **PR**ofessional **OF**fice **S**ystem) that operated in the mainframe environment. You could send text messages to other users with PROFS, but it was nothing like today's email systems. The only storage medium back then was floppy disks—which were literally floppy.

I had an advantage over many users because I had bought a Commodore SX-64 portable computer for home use several months earlier and had some experience with personal computers. Many employees, especially those who had been around for many years, resisted learning how to use these "newfangled" machines. Some eventually retired without ever using them.

The best thing about the new computers, for me, was that we could use the word processor to type a document and then print it on a (painfully slow) dot-matrix printer. This was a huge improvement over having to write documents longhand with a pen or pencil on paper, taking the handwritten document to a typing pool, and waiting at least one or two days for it to be returned in typewritten form. It also meant that we no longer had to physically cut, paste, and reassemble sections of a paper document if we needed to modify it and didn't want to start over from scratch.

One of the more fortunate decisions in my life was taking a typing class in high school. As a high school senior, I needed an elective to complete my course load and, for the sole reason that my mother was friends with the typing teacher, I chose that class over the others. Little did I know that I would spend much of the rest of my life typing on a keyboard (as I'm doing at this moment).

I also enjoyed it because I was the only male in the class. I did surprisingly well, going to the district typing contest (yes, that used to be a thing) and finishing with the fifth-fastest typing speed, at about 65–70 words per minute.

* * *

The spring and summer of 1984 were interesting times. The first Shuttle pad abort happened on June 26 of that year. During STS-41-D's launch attempt, there was a launch abort at T–6 seconds. Main engines No. 2 and No. 3 ignited briefly, but they cut off when main engine No. 1 failed to ignite.

There was a pad fire about ten minutes later. The fire was caused by hydrogen escaping from the engines, igniting combustible material on the Mobile Launch Platform. The flame from the burning hydrogen might have reached as high as the Shuttle's cockpit, but the crew would not have seen it because hydrogen burns cleanly (invisible to humans). If they had immediately opened the hatch to escape the Orbiter once the engines stopped, they might have run into the fire.

Mission Specialist Steve Hawley joked following the abort: "Gee, I thought we'd be a lot higher at MECO (Main Engine Cut-Off)!" After a 20-minute wait, the crew left the vehicle and was soaked by water from the pad's fire suppression system, activated because of the fire.

There would be four more pad aborts during the Shuttle Program, with the STS-68 abort in 1994 occurring at T-1.9 seconds—less than two seconds before the solid rocket boosters would have ignited.

Supercooled liquid oxygen and liquid hydrogen were used to fuel the Shuttle's main engines. Hydrogen is highly combustible, so if the liquid form evaporates back into a gas during storage, fueling, or flight, a leak could result in an explosion. Despite these dangers, NASA and other space agencies continue to use it as a fuel source due to its efficiency compared to alternatives.

NASA has a history of dealing with this hydrogen issue. The ground crew at KSC suffered through what they call "the summer of hydrogen" in 1990 when the Shuttle fleet was grounded for six months, from April to October, by a difficult-to-find hydrogen leak that prevented them from filling the Orbiter's external tank.

NASA employee demonstrating the "Broom Method" for finding hydrogen fires [NASA photo]

During the Apollo missions, NASA used a low-tech method for detecting hydrogen leaks. Someone would walk with a long broom held in front of them and if the broom came into contact with burning hydrogen, its end would burst into flames. It was not very sophisticated, but it worked.

During the Shuttle program, NASA tried using sensors to detect leaks and ultraviolet cameras to spot flames already burning, but they still did not provide an immediate visual sign of a leak. More recently, NASA collaborated with the Florida Solar Energy Center to develop a chemochromic tape that changes color in the presence of hydrogen by reacting with compounds in the outer layer of the tape.

Detecting hydrogen leaks remains a challenge today. In September 2022, NASA called off its second attempt to launch Artemis I, the first launch of the Space Launch System (SLS), after being unable to resolve a liquid hydrogen leak during fueling of the rocket, delaying launch until November 16, 2022.

* * *

On May 24, 1984, there was much excitement at JSC, at least among the male population, when Playboy model and cover girl Barbi Benton visited the Johnson Space Center. She was given a VIP tour unlike any I had seen before, surrounded by a group of JSC officials including an astronaut, a flight director, and several others (all men, of course). Among other activities, she tried on an astronaut flight suit and helmet and sat in the commander's seat in a Shuttle mockup cockpit during her visit.

* * *

In mid-September that year, Paramount Pictures filmed several scenes of the television miniseries *Space*, based on the James Michener novel of the same name, at Ellington Field and at JSC Buildings 30 and 32.

The cast included James Garner, Beau Bridges, Blair Brown, Bruce Dern, Harry Hamlin, and Michael York. They used several NASA employees, including me, as extras in the film. I had no spoken lines in the film, but I did appear in a couple of scenes. My role was acting as an aircraft mechanic.

Herb's Paramount Pictures ID badge for the filming of "Space" at JSC and Ellington Field

In one scene that made the cut, I was working under the wing of an airplane as Harry Hamlin and Beau Bridges walked by. You could see me from behind (my best side?) under the wing of an aircraft, pretending to be working on it.

* * *

In February, 1985, John Chisler, a co-worker and friend who had spent the previous 12 months at NASA Headquarters in Washington, D.C., on a special assignment, returned to JSC. He told me that when he left the position at Headquarters, his supervisor in Washington asked if he had any suggestions for someone to fill the position he was vacating. He gave them my name and recommended me for the position.

15 - Early Space Station At NASA Headquarters

The position at NASA Headquarters for which I had been recommended was in the new Space Station Program Office. It would be a one-year special assignment, similar to John Chisler's assignment, as the Space Station User Cost Manager.

I was copied on the letter dated January 29, 1985, that Phil Culbertson, Associate Administrator for Space Station at Headquarters, sent to JSC Director Gerry Griffin, requesting his approval to reassign me to this position. I would report to the Chief, Special Projects Branch, Utilization and Performance Requirements Division, Office of Space Station, at Headquarters. The letter specified a Statement of Duties for the position, which included:

- Mission set costing:

    Develop a method of costing missions (when no such costs exist within NASA Headquarters)

    Cost test each mission set that makes up the requirements and performance envelope

- Operations cost:

    Study Space Station operations cost and how it is affected by user services

    Study user life-cycle cost as it relates to the Space Station

The job primarily involved serving as an advocate for potential Space Station users in activities concerning utilization costs and pricing, and acting as the technical manager for two contracts focused on developing Space Station pricing approaches. I also served as a procurement adviser and edited "white papers" (research-based documents that provide information, analysis, and insight into a certain topic) for the Division and was occasionally asked to edit Congressional testimony for Associate Administrator Phil Culbertson.

To develop pricing structures, I was assigned to work with two economists at the Jet Propulsion Laboratory (JPL) in Pasadena, CA. The work involved developing algorithms and running repeated trials ("costing missions") on the JPL computers using different variables. In those early days of the Space Station Program, we made many assumptions about potential partners, customers, and how the Space Station would be utilized. I flew from Washington, D.C., to Pasadena monthly throughout that year to check in with the economists at JPL.

At the time, we had no idea that it would be another 15 years before a different version of the Space Station would be built and inhabited by a crew for the first time. So, even though the work we were doing was interesting and challenging, the results of our work eventually became mostly outdated before ISS operations began.

* * *

Our Space Station Program offices were in Federal Office Building (FOB)-10 located on Independence Avenue, just a few blocks from the National Air and Space Museum. A short 37-minute documentary about the Space Shuttle Program titled *The Dream is Alive* that was filmed in IMAX began showing at the Air and Space Museum in June that year. The film includes scenes from several Shuttle missions and is narrated by Walter Cronkite. I attended a pre-screening of the film for NASA employees and enjoyed it so much that I returned to the museum, a short walk from my office, several times to watch it again. Anytime I had friends or family visiting Washington, D.C., I would take them to see it. I still have a copy of the film on DVD and watch it occasionally.

* * *

I was lucky enough to have been sent to KSC for a meeting that summer during the period of an expected Shuttle launch. I watched Mission STS-51-G launch early in the morning of June 17, 1985. It was the 18th flight of the Shuttle Program and the 5th flight of Shuttle *Discovery*. Unfortunately, it was the only Shuttle launch I witnessed in person.

* * *

I had no knowledge of it at the time, but I've since learned about a strange episode that occurred on STS-51-B in early 1985. For obvious reasons, there has been little reporting on the subject. Chinese-born scientist Taylor Wang, designer of an experiment called the Drop Dynamics Module, was selected as a payload specialist for that flight.

Despite Wang working on the experiment for almost a decade, it did not work when he turned on his instrument. Because time is limited on Shuttle missions, every crew member follows a detailed timeline, with a long list of tasks to perform during their day. Wang asked flight controllers if they would allow him time to diagnose the problem in the hope of repairing his experiment. Flight controllers were reluctant to agree.

Wang became frustrated and depressed as a result of the problems he was experiencing with his experiment and difficulties with the flight controllers. He allegedly threatened to "not go back" if they did not allow him time to repair his experiment.

After that comment, NASA feared that he might be mentally unstable. Commander Bob Overmyer believed that he was fine, but feeling frustrated about the failure of his experiment.

Based on comments from a few Shuttle commanders found in the JSC Oral History Project, it's possible to piece together some of the story:

John Fabian, who was a mission specialist on the next Shuttle flight, in his JSC Oral History Project interview, stated:

> "We put a lock on the door of the side hatch. It was installed when we got into orbit so that the door could not be opened from the inside and commit hari-kari, killing the whole crew. That was not because of anybody we had on our flight but because of a concern about someone who had flown before 51-G."

Brewster Shaw was commander for STS-61-B, which flew seven months after Wang's mission. In his JSC Oral History Project interview, he stated:

> "I remember I got this padlock, and when we got on orbit, I went down to the hatch on the side of the Orbiter, and I padlocked the hatch control so that you could not open the hatch. I mean, on the Orbiter in orbit you can go down there and you just flip this little thing and you crank that handle once, the hatch opens and all the air goes out and everybody goes out with it, just like that. And I thought to myself, 'Jeez, I don't know this guy very well. He might flip out or something.' So I padlocked the hatch shut right after we got on orbit, and I didn't take

the padlock off until we were in de-orbit prep. I don't know if I was supposed to do that or not, but that's a decision I made as being responsible for my crew and I just did it."

When the Shuttle returned to flight after the *Challenger* accident, a Side Hatch Locking Device (a small clamp fitting over the locking lever on the hatch handle) was formally implemented "to prevent the hatch from being inadvertently unlocked while in orbit," according to updated NASA guidelines.

* * *

Throughout my career at NASA, I read and heard about numerous instances where a private citizen sent NASA a letter, usually handwritten, notifying us that we didn't know what we were doing, that our Space Shuttle or Space Station design was all wrong, and that they had a much better design. I received such a letter in September 1985 from a private citizen in Kentucky.

He offered to sell his plans for a doughnut-shaped space station to NASA for 5% of the $8 billion cost of Space Station Freedom (a bargain at $400 million!). I still have a copy of that letter. Here are a few of the statements in the four-page letter that provide a summary of his message:

- "We can use this letter as a contract agreement."

- "The way you're going about designing this space station is way off track!"

- "Look at the time wasted when each piece has to be scent (sic) into space. My design is in one doughnut shaped module which has all the needed elements inside this one module!"

- "Scend (sic) me the funds to come to your headquarters before this letter has time to dry."

- "Your agency does not have the same technology as me. Your (sic) going to have to have my help because of this."

- "I know how to put the entire building in space in one launch."

- "Well sirs I would like to tell you more but your agency has not paid for this technology in this letter yet so why should a person tell you all the answers before you pay."

- "So now sirs its goodbuy (sic) until your agency scends (sic) the due funds."

Sounds legit, right?

* * *

The last day of my one-year assignment at Headquarters would be Friday, January 31, 1986. My co-workers had planned a going-away party for me to be held that Friday.

On Tuesday, January 28, at 11:39 a.m., Shuttle *Challenger*, on Mission STS-51-L, launched. Seventy-three seconds later, *Challenger* broke apart. All seven crew members perished. It is difficult to describe what it was like at NASA Headquarters that morning.

I thought back to the Apollo 1 fire that occurred, eerily, on January 27, 1967, almost exactly 19 years earlier to the day. Everyone in the Headquarters building was shaken and devastated by what we had just witnessed on television. The worst feeling that morning was one of helplessness.

What should we do? What COULD we do? What do we say to each other? No one felt like trying to get any work done for the rest of the day. It was hard to concentrate. We all were sitting with blank stares on our faces or walking around like zombies. As no one was in the mood for any form of celebration, my going-away party planned for that Friday was canceled.

I had not worked with any of the astronauts we lost that day, but I had met Judy Resnik, one of the Mission Specialists on the flight. In the early 1980s, Judy and I often worked out in the same aerobics class on Saturday mornings at a local health club, just a few miles from JSC.

Judy became a NASA astronaut at the age of 29 in 1978, with a PhD in electrical engineering. She was one of six women accepted into the program in that astronaut class. Judy's first flight had taken place aboard the maiden voyage of Shuttle *Discovery*. She became the second American woman to fly in space, after Sally Ride.

* * *

There was obviously much activity at the Kennedy Space Center that morning, where the accident happened. Astronaut Mike Coats, whom I would have the opportunity to work for when he became JSC Director in 2005, flew to KSC two hours after the accident and spent the next four months there working on the recovery effort.

Search-and-rescue aircraft from Patrick Air Force Base were involved, and the Coast Guard began one of the largest surface searches in its history—a rectangle 58 miles wide and 155 miles long.

When the *Columbia* accident occurred 17 years later, in 2003, it was on a Saturday morning when most employees were at home for the weekend. As heart-wrenching as that *Columbia* accident was, those of us not involved in the recovery effort had a couple of days to process what had happened before we had to return to work.

16 - Back to Space Station at JSC

I returned to work at JSC on February 3, 1986, and was assigned to the Space Station Procurement Office. Rather than managing all development efforts at one location, NASA decided to divide the Space Station Program into four segments called Work Packages, spread across multiple NASA centers. JSC was one of those four centers.

In April 1985, NASA competitively awarded multiple contracts to various aerospace companies to support the initial work under each of these Work Packages.

Work Package 1, managed by Marshall Space Flight Center, covered the definition and preliminary design of pressurized "common" modules; node structures; environmental control systems; laboratory module outfitting; logistics modules; engine elements within the propulsion system; and Orbital Maneuvering Vehicles and Orbital Transfer Vehicle accommodations. Separate contracts to support this effort were awarded to Boeing and Martin Marietta.

Work Package 2, managed by JSC, covered the definition and preliminary design of the structural framework to which the elements of the Space Station would be attached; crewed systems with the habitat module; the interface between the Space Station and the Space Shuttle; mechanisms, such as Remote Manipulator Systems; node outfitting with attitude control, thermal control, communications, propulsion and data management subsystems; airlocks, and extravehicular activity accommodations. Separate contracts to support this effort were awarded to McDonnell Douglas and Rockwell.

Work Package 3, managed by Goddard Space Flight Center, covered the definition and preliminary design of the automated free-flying platforms and NASA's role in the development of provisions to service, maintain, and repair the platforms and other free-flying spacecraft; the flight telerobotic system; and provisions for instruments and payloads to be attached externally to the Space Station. Separate contracts to support this effort were awarded to RCA Astro Electronics and General Electric.

Work Package 4, managed by Lewis Research Center (later renamed Glenn Research Center at Lewis Field in 1999), covered the definition and preliminary design of the electrical power-generating, conditioning, and storage systems. Separate contracts to support this effort were awarded to Rockwell and TRW.

NASA Administrator James Beggs was the Source Selection Official and made the final selection decision for all of the contract awards at the same time—except those for Work Package 2. JSC had received proposals from McDonnell Douglas, Rockwell, and Lockheed. The competition was too close for Beggs to call and required additional consideration by JSC's Source Evaluation Board (SEB) before the final awards could be made.

The weaknesses of each of the three proposals were reviewed and questions were developed for each proposer to clarify certain points. The companies were asked to respond to their questions. The schedule for meeting with each company was literally determined by drawing straws. On their assigned days, each company responded to the questions, and the process was repeated several times until the SEB felt it had enough data to send to Beggs for his final selections. Beggs eventually selected McDonnell Douglas and Rockwell.

Lockheed later teamed with McDonnell on its Work Package 2 contract.

The Kennedy Space Center was given the responsibility for preflight and launch operations. KSC would also be involved in logistics support activities. Other NASA centers would also support the definition and preliminary design activities.

After the initial definition and preliminary design effort was completed, the two contractors at each center submitted proposals for the single contract to be awarded at each center for the DDT&E phase of the work.

The eventually selected contractors for each Work Package (WP) were:

- Work Package 1 - Boeing

- Work Package 2 - McDonnell Douglas

- Work Package 3 - General Electric

- Work Package 4 - Rocketdyne

When I first returned to JSC, I was assigned to help administer the McDonnell Douglas WP-2 contract. Then, on June 9, 1986, the Rogers Commission, released its report. The Rogers Commission, chaired by William Rogers, was directed by President Reagan to investigate the *Challenger* accident. The committee also included Neil Armstrong and Sally Ride. The accident and the resulting report caused a lot of turmoil within NASA.

The Rogers Commission determined that the accident was caused by a failure of the O-rings on the right solid rocket booster. The failure resulted in hot gases blowing by the O-ring and causing structural failure of the external tank.

The Commission found that NASA managers knew that the O-rings' design was flawed and that their failure could be catastrophic. The report also criticized the lead center concept in the Shuttle Program, which positions the Program Manager at a center rather than at Headquarters. The Commission wanted Headquarters to take tighter control and bring the centers under its direction. As a result, Headquarters reassessed the management structure of the Space Station Program before beginning the design and development phase.

An independent committee, headed by General Sam Phillips, who had directed the Apollo program, was formed to evaluate the existing management structure. Phillips's study also investigated the distribution of work among the centers and evaluated NASA's plan for in-house systems engineering and integration.

During the Apollo Program, Headquarters had exercised the program management function, so it was no surprise when Phillips's committee recommended restructuring the Station Program so that the Program Office would be responsible to management at Headquarters, rather than being part of JSC, as was currently the case.

The committee also recommended that NASA acquire a contractor experienced in systems engineering and integration to support the new Program Office, which would be managed by Headquarters. NASA Administrator James Fletcher accepted the recommendations. Andy Stofan, who was the director at Lewis Research Center at the time, was chosen to become the new Associate Administrator for Space Station at NASA Headquarters.

At JSC, the decision to relocate the Space Station Program Office worried those employees working in program management. The decision could mean they would be taken out of their current assignments and put in other jobs, either at JSC or near Washington, D.C. Many of those JSC employees were unwilling to move. Administrator Fletcher visited each of the centers to explain the upcoming changes.

I attended the meeting Fletcher held at JSC in the Teague Auditorium, packed with employees. I was shocked at how openly hostile to Fletcher many employees were as they expressed their frustrations. I had never seen a NASA administrator treated in that way, before or since. None of this caused Fletcher to change his plans.

As the Phillips committee recommended, NASA planned to award a major contract for systems engineering and integration services to an experienced aerospace company that would support the Station Program Office. Searching for a location for the new Station Program Office that was near, but not in, Washington, D.C., NASA conducted a competition among several locations in the Washington, D.C., vicinity.

The decision was made to select Reston, VA, approximately 20 miles from NASA Headquarters, as the new home for the Space Station Program Office. The site in Reston would be far enough outside D.C. to, at least somewhat, protect the Station Program management from the pressures of the Capital but close enough that traveling from one to the other was a short trip.

I didn't realize it at the time, but these decisions would significantly impact me. Soon after the decisions were announced, I received an unforgettable phone call. The caller was Admiral Stu Evans, the Assistant Administrator for Procurement at NASA Headquarters, whom I had met only briefly during my 1-year assignment at Headquarters the previous year.

The conversation went something like this: "Herb, you've probably heard that NASA plans to award a new contract for engineering support to the Space Station Program Office and that, since the Program Office will now be managed by Headquarters instead of JSC, the procurement will be the responsibility of our procurement office here at Headquarters. My problem is that these folks here in D.C. have never bought much more than toilet paper and pencils. I need someone with experience working on major program contracts to do this job."

"We're planning to form a Source Evaluation Board, with members from multiple centers to be hosted at KSC. I'd like you to be the contracting officer for that SEB at KSC. You would report to KSC in Florida to work on the SEB and, after you've made a selection, move here to D.C. to negotiate, award, and manage the contract. Would you be interested in doing that for me?"

I was young, still single, and always ready for a new adventure, but I had not been expecting nor prepared for this phone call. I considered the offer for a few seconds and replied: "Yes, sir. I will do that." After hanging up the phone, I convinced myself that, for the sake of my future NASA career, I had made the right decision.

After only eight months back in Houston, I would head to Kennedy Space Center in Florida in October. A memory from that short period back in Houston was meeting John Aaron who, as the EECOM during Apollo 12, saved that mission with his "SCE to Aux" call. Aaron was the acting Space Station Program Manager at JSC, and he chaired many technical meetings I attended during that time.

17 - Program Support Contract SEB at KSC

In October 1986, I headed to Florida. My assignment was to serve as the contracting officer and member of the Business Evaluation Committee for the Space Station Program Support Contract (PSC) Source Evaluation Board (SEB). When I left JSC, I officially became a NASA Headquarters employee, though I reported to KSC instead of Washington, D.C.

The SEB was an agency-wide group that included members from Headquarters, JSC, KSC, MSFC, Goddard Space Flight Center, Lewis Research Center (now Glenn Research Center), and Langley Research Center. Norm Chaffee, a fellow employee from JSC, was appointed chairman of the Technical Evaluation Committee. Chaffee had worked on the Mercury, Gemini, Apollo, ASTP, Skylab, and Space Shuttle programs since 1962.

The SEB Chairman was Andy Pickett, the KSC deputy director, who had previous experience chairing an SEB. When NASA Administrator James Fletcher asked Pickett to chair the SEB, Pickett told him, "I will only chair this board if we can do it at Kennedy Space Center. I don't want to leave home for a year to do this."

The administrator said, "Okay. You can have it wherever you want." In addition to having the KSC deputy director serving on our board, the KSC Director of Procurement, Wes Dean, was serving as the chair of our Business Evaluation Committee.

Herb (2nd from right) with the PSC Business Evaluation Committee outside secure SEB facility at Cape Canaveral Air Force Station in 1987

BUSINESS COMMITTEE

Wesley H. Dean, Chairman	KSC	SI-PRO
Thomas Smith. Co-Chairman	MSFC	AP14
Herbert H. Baker, Jr., Contracting Officer	HQ	HWD
Gloria D'Elousa, Secretary	KSC	SI-PRO
E. Joyce Smith, Part-Time	KSC	SI-PRO

EVALUATORS

Marianne Bachstein	KSC	SI-PRO-61
Patricia Beall	KSC	SI-PRO-5
Sheri Thornton	GSFC	403.0
Oscar Gamboa	KSC	EO
Norman Perry	KSC	SI-PRO-4

After having lived most of my life in and around a city as large as Houston, I chose not to move to one of the beach towns—like Titusville, Cocoa Beach, or Melbourne—near KSC, and instead found an apartment on the southeast side of Orlando, just north of the airport. It was a fairly long (50 miles) but pleasant drive each day on the Bee Line Expressway (now called the Beachline Expressway) to KSC. Because we needed a secure facility for the SEB, the building that housed us was on the adjacent Cape Canaveral Air Force Station (CCAFS), a short drive east of KSC.

I've been involved in many SEBs throughout my career. Most last approximately one year from start to finish, but some have taken 1½ to 2 years (or longer) to complete. Our SEB convened in mid-October and since most of our members were on a temporary assignment and lived in other states, we were determined to complete our job within 9 months, by July 1987. To stay on schedule, we sometimes worked until 1:30 or 2:00 a.m., something I had never done regularly before.

For me, that meant arriving back at my apartment at 2:30 to 3:00 a.m. on those long days, sleeping for just 2 or 3 hours, and returning to CCAFS by 8:00 a.m. the next morning. There were many days when we didn't take a break for dinner. We would order takeout, and one of the support staff would pick it up for us. We would continue working while we had dinner. On those nights when we worked past midnight, we would have someone pick up pizza or calzones from an all-night restaurant to keep us fueled.

Despite the long hours, working with Andy Pickett was a pleasure, and he kept morale high. Andy was a classic "good ole boy." He grew up in rural Alabama and used phrases like, "I opine that…" and "If I had my druthers…" However, he was very smart and had a mind like a steel trap. When he wanted to have a Board meeting, he would blow into his train whistle which could be heard throughout our building.

The whistle was a 9-inch-long rectangular block that had been carved for him by a craftsman in Tennessee. When you heard the whistle, you dropped what you were doing and headed to the conference room. When the Board's work was completed, he gifted all of us our own whistle, which I proudly display in my office today.

Since this effort was not a follow-on or an extension of an existing contract, we were starting from scratch. We released a draft Request for Proposal (RFP) to industry in late November and, after incorporating changes suggested by potential offerors, the formal RFP was released on February 3. Two weeks later, we held a pre-proposal conference attended by representatives from 60 companies.

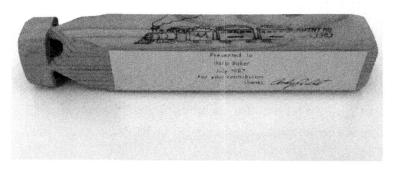

Train whistle presented to Herb for his contribution to the PSC (SEB), a copy of the whistle used by the SEB Chairperson, Andy Pickett.

A due date for proposals of April 3, 1987, was established. Proposals from Grumman and TRW were received on the due date. The Grumman team included Ford Aerospace and Booz Allen & Hamilton as partners. The TRW team included Lockheed Missiles & Space and Teledyne Brown Engineering as partners.

Before our SEB activity began, the NASA administrator had made the decision to exclude Space Station Work Package hardware competitors (e.g., Boeing, Lockheed Martin, McDonnell Douglas, Rockwell) from competing for this Program Support Contract as either a prime or subcontractor, to avoid any conflicts of interest.

Our RFP had included a provision stating that a proposal from a Phase C/D Work Package prime contract competitor would not be considered by our SEB. In addition, we included a clause in the RFP forbidding the PSC contractor from using a Work Package prime contractor as a PSC subcontractor or partner.

This worked in our favor because it limited the number of potential offerors. Receiving just two proposals ensured that there would be competition but also meant that we had to evaluate and choose between just two companies.

Soon after our RFP was released, I received another one of those letters from a private citizen who informed me that he had a prefabricated Space Station design patent pending and wanted instructions for submitting his plans rather than responding to the requirements in our RFP.

His correspondence was not quite as bizarre as the letter proposing the doughnut-shaped Space Station, but it was just as painful to read due to the same types of spelling and grammatical errors and wild declarations. He received a polite response from me declining his offer and referring him back to the clear requirements of our RFP.

The next three months, spent evaluating the proposed costs and strengths and weaknesses of the two proposals, were the most work-intensive of our stay in Florida. On July 1, 1987, several members of our SEB, including me, traveled to NASA Headquarters to present our recommendations to the NASA Administrator, James Fletcher, who was the Source Selection Official.

The following day, Administrator Fletcher announced that he had selected Grumman for award of the PSC Contract, with an estimated value of $891 million over the expected 10-year period of performance.

* * *

Meanwhile, back at JSC—after working for a year to recover from the *Challenger* accident—Dan Brandenstein, who was then Chief of the Astronaut Office, thought it might be a good idea for JSC to hold a 1950s style sock-hop to boost morale. Back in the 1950's, high school dances were usually held in gyms. The students would remove their shoes and dance in their socks so that they wouldn't scratch the gym's hardwood floor.

I spoke recently with retired astronaut Brewster Shaw at an event at the Remembering *Columbia* Museum, and he told me that it all began when he, Hoot Gibson, and George "Pinky" Nelson started having jam sessions in an aircraft hangar.

Shaw had suggested putting together a band for the sock-hop, and Gibson thought it was a great idea. Once they met to rehearse, they found that none of the group wanted to play lead guitar. Gibson finally agreed to do it.

Next, they needed a drummer. Jim Wetherbee had a drum set, but he had not played it in years. He was invited to the rehearsal that night anyway.

The band's performance at the sock-hop turned out to be a great success. They called themselves Max Q, which is a rocket launch term referring to maximum dynamic pressure and maximum noise.

The band also performed at a Fajita Festival—an annual event held by NASA's Mission Operations Directorate. For that performance, astronaut Steve Hawley joined the group as their keyboard player.

The original band members are now all retired; however new groups of astronaut musicians have kept the band alive. As members leave the band, others are recruited to take their place.

NASA's Astronaut Selection Board sometimes asked potential candidates if they played a musical instrument.

Approximately fifty percent of NASA's astronauts play a musical instrument, but only a few have joined Max Q. Rick Husband, commander of the ill-fated *Columbia* mission, had a nice singing voice, but he was more into church hymns. Former JSC Director Ellen Ochoa was a flute player with Stanford's symphony orchestra but she prefers classical music.

Since 2003, there has been a second astronaut band, called Bandella. This band primarily plays folk, Americana, and bluegrass music. The band originally got together in Star City, Russia, where several of its members trained with the Russian space program.

Bandella still performs occasionally in the Houston area with its original members:

- Chris Hadfield, retired Canadian astronaut and bandleader. Hadfield is well known for performing a cover of David Bowie's *Space Oddity* while on the ISS.
- Cady Coleman, retired NASA astronaut, who plays the flute and has often played with the Irish band, *The Chieftains*
- Steve Robinson, retired NASA astronaut who plays acoustic lead guitar, banjo, and stand-up bass
- Dan Burbank, retired NASA astronaut, who sings vocals and is a guitar/bass player
- Micki Pettit, wife of retired astronaut Don Pettit, who brings a big jazz-&-show tune voice to the group

I most recently saw Bandella playing at an event at Space Center Houston in early 2020.

Herb with Cady Coleman at a Bandella performance

* * *

Did you know that it's no coincidence that the Space Coast region, Brevard County area, in Florida, has a telephone area code of 321, like a countdown? (When I lived in Florida in the 1980s, my phone number's area code in Orlando and at KSC was *407*.)

In the 1990s, Brevard County's population was growing rapidly. A Titusville resident and self-professed space geek named Ozzie Osband came up with the idea for the new area code for the "countdown capital." He petitioned the Florida Public Service Commission in 1998 and received approval to implement the new area code.

The new *321* area code went into effect on November 1, 1999, and on that same day, Florida Governor Jeb Bush made the first call to KSC. KSC deputy director James Jennings answered the call, with Osband sitting beside him.

18 - Working with Fred Haise

Since retiring from NASA in January 2017, I have given many speeches, presentations, and interviews, and I am often asked, "What is your favorite memory from your NASA career?" It's not easy to pick only one from those 40+ years, but my response is usually, "Working with Apollo 13 astronaut Fred Haise in the 1980s."

When Grumman was selected by Administrator Fletcher for the award of the Program Support Contract, the company appointed Fred as the president of its new Space Station Program Support Division. He would be responsible for managing the systems engineering and integration effort that Grumman would provide to the Space Station Program Office, which was newly located in Reston, VA.

When Fred retired from NASA in June 1979, after serving as the commander and successfully flying the Space Shuttle *Enterprise* in the Approach and Landing Tests, he joined Grumman Aerospace Corporation as Vice President of Space Programs. As a Lunar Module Pilot for NASA, he had spent a considerable amount of time working with Grumman, the company responsible for designing and delivering the Lunar Modules to NASA. In 1983, he was appointed president of Grumman Technical Services.

Under the new Program Support Contract, with four different Work Packages managed by four different NASA centers, it would be Grumman's responsibility to monitor the various activities and ensure that the parts would fit together and function properly once in space.

AWARD/CONTRACT	1. THIS CONTRACT IS A RATED ORDER UNDER DPAS (15 CFR 350)		RATING N/A	PAGE OF PAGES

2. CONTRACT (Proc. Inst. Ident.) NO. NASW-4300	3. EFFECTIVE DATE July 31, 1987	4. REQUISITION/PURCHASE REQUEST/PROJECT NO. 10-41911

5. ISSUED BY	CODE HWD

NASA Headquarters
Contracts and Grants Division
Code HW
Washington, DC 20546

6. ADMINISTERED BY (If other than Item 5) CODE

7. NAME AND ADDRESS OF CONTRACTOR (No., street, city, county, State and ZIP Code)

Grumman Aerospace Corporation
Space Station Program Support Division
South Oyster Bay Road
Bethpage, NY 11714

8. DELIVERY
[ ] FOB ORIGIN [ ] OTHER (See below)
9. DISCOUNT FOR PROMPT PAYMENT

10. SUBMIT INVOICES (4 copies unless otherwise specified) TO THE ADDRESS SHOWN IN: ITEM

CODE	FACILITY CODE
11. SHIP TO/MARK FOR	CODE NASW-4300

12. PAYMENT WILL BE MADE BY CODE BFH

NASA Headquarters
Financial Management Division
Washington, DC 20546

13. AUTHORITY FOR USING OTHER THAN FULL AND OPEN COMPETITION:
[ ] 10 U.S.C. 2304(c)( ) [ ] 41 U.S.C. 253(c)( )

14. ACCOUNTING AND APPROPRIATION DATA
80 7/8 0108

15A. ITEM NO.	15B. SUPPLIES/SERVICES	15C. QUANTITY	15D. UNIT	15E. UNIT PRICE	15F. AMOUNT
	APPROVED Space Station Program Support Contract (PSC) Assistant Administrator for Procurement July 31, 1987 Date				$891,233,260

15G. TOTAL AMOUNT OF CONTRACT ▶ $

16. TABLE OF CONTENTS

(✓)	SEC.	DESCRIPTION	PAGE(S)	(✓)	SEC.	DESCRIPTION	PAGE(S)
		PART I — THE SCHEDULE				PART II — CONTRACT CLAUSES	
X	A	SOLICITATION/CONTRACT FORM	4	X	I	CONTRACT CLAUSES	18
X	B	SUPPLIES OR SERVICES AND PRICES/COSTS	6			PART III — LIST OF DOCUMENTS, EXHIBITS AND OTHER ATTACH.	
X	C	DESCRIPTION/SPECS./WORK STATEMENT	1	X	J	LIST OF ATTACHMENTS	180
X	D	PACKAGING AND MARKING	1			PART IV — REPRESENTATIONS AND INSTRUCTIONS	
X	E	INSPECTION AND ACCEPTANCE	1		K	REPRESENTATIONS, CERTIFICATIONS AND OTHER STATEMENTS OF OFFERORS	
X	F	DELIVERIES OR PERFORMANCE	2				
X	G	CONTRACT ADMINISTRATION DATA	7		L	INSTRS., CONDS., AND NOTICES TO OFFERORS	
X	H	SPECIAL CONTRACT REQUIREMENTS	11		M	EVALUATION FACTORS FOR AWARD	

CONTRACTING OFFICER WILL COMPLETE ITEM 17 OR 18 AS APPLICABLE

17. [X] CONTRACTOR'S NEGOTIATED AGREEMENT (Contractor is required to sign this document and return ____ copies to issuing office.) Contractor agrees to furnish and deliver all items or perform all the services set forth or otherwise identified above and on any continuation sheets for the consideration stated herein. The rights and obligations of the parties to this contract shall be subject to and governed by the following documents: (a) this award/contract, (b) the solicitation, if any, and (c) such provisions, representations, certifications, and specifications, as are attached or incorporated by reference herein. (Attachments are listed herein.)	18. [ ] AWARD (Contractor is not required to sign this document.) Your offer on Solicitation Number ____ including the additions or changes made by you which additions or changes are set forth in full above, is hereby accepted as to the items listed above and on any continuation sheets. This award consummates the contract which consists of the following documents: (a) the Government's solicitation and your offer, and (b) this award/contract. No further contractual document is necessary.

19A. NAME AND TITLE OF SIGNER (Type or print) Fred W. Haise, President Space Station Program Support Division	20A. NAME OF CONTRACTING OFFICER Herbert H. Baker, Jr.
19B. NAME OF CONTRACTOR BY (Signature of person authorized to sign)	19C. DATE SIGNED 7/20/87	20B. UNITED STATES OF AMERICA BY (Signature of Contracting Officer)	20C. DATE SIGNED July 31, 1987

NSN 7540-01-152-8069
PREVIOUS EDITION UNUSABLE

26-107

STANDARD FORM 26 (REV. 4-85)
Prescribed by GSA
FAR (48 CFR) 53.214(a)

Cover page of the Space Station Program Support Contract negotiated and signed by Fred Haise for Grumman and Herb for NASA

As Fred described it at the time, "We are the check and balance for the various systems. Each contractor has a model of what they are working on, but we are the only ones who have a technical model of the entire vehicle—the only ones who have the whole puzzle together."

Once the selection of Grumman was announced and our SEB activities were completed, I moved out of my apartment in Orlando and relocated to Reston. The Space Station Program Office would be moving into a brand-new facility that was still being built in Reston, called Parkridge III, just seven miles east of Dulles Airport. I moved into an apartment a short five-minute drive from that new office space. I had never had such a short commute to any job, and Reston was a beautiful planned community. The concept of the planned community was that people would live, work, and play within the community. It certainly worked for me.

Once I was settled in Reston, my first task was to meet with Fred and two other Grumman representatives, business managers Pat Curran and Alex Harrisiadis, to negotiate the dollar value and other details of the PSC contract. It was an interesting and exciting time for me. Not only was I starting a new job as a contracting officer for NASA Headquarters and moving to a new home, I was excited about negotiating a 10-year Space Station contract worth nearly $1 billion with one of my heroes. I had covered Apollo 13 with the news media as it happened in 1970, and several years later, I was a full-time NASA employee at JSC while Fred was flying the Approach and Landing Tests in Shuttle *Enterprise*.

The fact that I had been officially assigned to Headquarters but reported to KSC when I left Houston to do a procurement-sensitive job in a secure facility resulted in a strange situation. Since I was technically a Headquarters employee while at KSC, my supervisor "on paper" was in Washington, D.C. However, he was not involved in the SEB and had not been given the clearance to know anything about the procurement sensitive/confidential work I was involved in. The only person at Headquarters with that SEB clearance was the guy at the very top of my organization, the Assistant Administrator for Procurement, Admiral Stu Evans.

Before I could begin negotiations with Grumman, I had some work to do. I had to plan a negotiation strategy that included, among other elements, a dollar range for the contract value within which I would have the authority to agree to with Grumman. Over most of my career, getting approval for that "Pre-Negotiation Position" (or PNP as we called it in the procurement world) would have involved multiple presentations, over multiple days, to at least 15-20 people (including lawyers, engineers, and budget analysts), especially at this high dollar value. But in this case, the only person at Headquarters who had both knowledge of and the necessary clearances for what I was working on was Admiral Evans.

Rather than making a lengthy presentation to a room full of people to get the approval I needed to begin negotiations, I simply sat alone with Evans on the sofa in his corner office, my work papers spread over his coffee table in front of us. With just the two of us in his office, I thought back to that unexpected call from him one year earlier when he asked me to do exactly the job I was doing at that moment.

Admiral Evans asked just a few questions that were easily answered, and he approved the negotiation position that I had proposed without requiring a single change. The meeting lasted less than 30 minutes. The next day, I contacted Grumman and arranged to meet with them to begin negotiations.

I don't recall any sticking points in our negotiations, but the complexity of the contract, the details in the 120-page work description (Statement of Work), the use of an escalation clause to determine changes to the contract value based on the Consumer Price Index, and the many other terms and conditions of the contract required several days of negotiations.

The escalation clause, using the Consumer Price Index, was considered necessary because the contract was just over ten years in length. Most Government contracts are five years, or less, in length. It's much more difficult to predict economic factors, such as inflation, over ten years as compared to five years. This adjustment clause would protect both Grumman and the Government from any unexpected major changes in the economy over the life of the contract.

Once we finished negotiating the cost/fee and all the other necessary terms and conditions, we shook hands to close the deal, and the four of us—Fred, Pat, Alex, and I—went out to celebrate. It was my first opportunity to chat informally with Fred, and I was, naturally, hoping to hear some of his Apollo 13 stories. That night at dinner, it didn't take long for me to get the feeling that Fred preferred talking about his test pilot adventures. He rolled up the sleeve of his shirt to show me the burn scars on his arm from a 1974 plane crash in Galveston, which he survived, suffering second- and third-degree burns over 65% of his body. He spent 11 weeks in the hospital recovering from that accident, but thankfully was able to fly again.

* * *

Once the 227-page contract had been printed and reviewed by our management and legal counsel, Fred signed the contract for Grumman, and I signed it for NASA. After the contract had been executed, I immediately left for a much-needed vacation in Pittsburgh, PA, assuming it would take Grumman at least a couple of weeks to move its employees to Virginia and set up offices before being ready to start performing the contract work.

The contract was structured so that all work performed under the contract's Statement of Work had to be authorized by a written Task Order signed by the contracting officer (me, in this case). To my surprise, just one week after the contract was executed, I got a call where I was staying in Pittsburgh to let me know that Grumman was prepared to begin work. Task Orders specifying the work to be done had been prepared by the Program Office, but they needed my signature.

Unlike today, in the 1980s we didn't have the capability for electronic signatures, and email was in its infancy. To my relief, rather than asking me to fly back to Reston, the caller offered to have someone from NASA fly from Washington, D.C., to Pittsburgh International Airport with the Task Orders so that I could sign them there. I agreed and the next day we met at one of the gates at the airport (back in the days when a boarding pass wasn't required to go to airport gates) and I signed a stack of Task Orders that authorized Grumman to begin work. The courier took the next plane back to Virginia with the Task Orders in hand, and I returned to my vacation.

The president and CEO of Grumman, Jack O'Brien, was so proud of this Space Station support contract his company had just competitively won that he invited Fred, Dick Kline (Fred's deputy), Admiral Evans, and me to Bethpage, NY, to pose for a photo in his office that would be published on the front page of the August edition of GrummanWorld, the company newsletter. The two Grumman business managers involved in the negotiations, Pat Curran and Alex Harrisiadis, were also in the photo. The thing I remember most about that day was having lunch with that group in their corporate Executive Dining Room, a first for me.

NASA Pact Signed

On August 7, Grumman President John O'Brien and Assistant NASA Administrator Stu Evans signed the contract naming Grumman as Space Station Program Support Contractor for NASA.

Grumman will help manage the design and development of the space station. The new division will be responsible for ensuring once the space station hardware goes into orbit that all the components come together and work properly.

Present at the signing were (L to R): Dick Kline, vice president, Grumman Space Station Program Support Division; Division President Fred Haise; Herb Baker, NASA procurement contracting officer; O'Brien; Pat Curran, Division business manager; Alex Harrisiadis, Division business operations manager; and Evans.

Photo published on front page of Grumman company newsletter announcing award of Space Station support contract in 1987.

The Space Station Program was starting reasonably well; however, numerous problems would arise over the next six years. In 1988, an intergovernmental agreement was signed with Canada, the European Space Agency, and Japan. This international partnership proved to be invaluable. Also in 1988,

Congress decided that the Space Station would have to be built from existing technologies to reduce costs and risks. Congress demanded another redesign in 1990 and in 1991, they cut the budget for Space Station from $2.5 billion to $1.9 billion.

In 1993, the Program survived an attempt to cancel it in the House of Representatives by just one vote. Following this, the Program was restructured and the Program Office moved from Reston back to JSC. Russia was integrated into the Program as the fifth partner and the project became the International Space Station (ISS).

* * *

I missed most of that turmoil in the Program because, after just one year of administering the PSC contract in Reston, I was promoted to a supervisory position in the Headquarters Procurement Management Division, and I left the Space Station Program Office in Reston to work in downtown D.C., in 1988.

Unfortunately for Fred, he was trying to manage his Grumman team through a hopeless situation. Congress was continually reducing the Station's budget, causing constant restructuring of the Program to prevent schedule slippage.

A seemingly constant turnover in NASA management made matters worse. During Fred's four years on the Program, there were three different NASA administrators, three different Associate Administrators for Space Station at Headquarters, and three different Space Station Program Managers in Reston.

Somewhat to his relief, Fred was replaced in Reston by Tom Kelly in 1991. In his book *Never Panic Early*, Fred writes of a purely coincidental meeting with Dr. Chris Kraft at a gas station in Colorado Springs in 1986. (What a small world!) Fred mentioned to Kraft that he was thinking of bidding on the PSC contract. Hearing this, Kraft responded with his opinion that program management in Washington would not work and added, "Haise, you are crazy if you make that bid." Fred thought about that chance meeting often over the next four years.

Fred adds in his book that he considers those years in Reston, working on Space Station Freedom, to be "my time in purgatory." Fred and I have been acquainted now for over 35 years and I consider him a friend. We're both living in the Houston area and I see him occasionally at JSC. I've always thought it was ironic that while he was going through such a difficult period in his career, having the opportunity to work with him during that period (1987-1988) was a highlight of my career.

Herb's NASA ID badges for the Apollo and Skylab missions he covered working for television networks at the Manned Spacecraft Center from 1969 through 1974.

Alan Shepard setting up his microphone in preparation for an interview in the ABC-TV studio at the Manned Spacecraft Center

Herb with (L to R) Gerry Griffin, Vance Brand, Walt Cunningham, and Fred Haise at an Astronaut Scholarship Foundation event in 2018

Tree dedicated to Neil Armstrong in the Astronaut Memorial Grove at JSC. It appears to be the largest and oldest tree in the Grove and is the only tree with a boot print.

Fred Haise speaking at the Tree Dedication Ceremony for Walt Cunningham at the Astronaut Memorial Grove at JSC in 2023

Herb and friends having dinner with Fred Haise at Frenchie's Italian restaurant near JSC. Frenchie's has been owned by Francesco "Frankie" Camera (in the apron) for over 40 years

Herb next to the five F-1 engines on the first stage of the Saturn V vehicle in the George W. S. Abbey Rocket Park at Johnson Space Center

Herb with Nancy Conrad, widow of Pete Conrad, at the Space Exploration Educators Conference (SEEC) at Space Center Houston in 2024

Herb participating on a panel at the KSC Visitor Complex IMAX Theater immediately prior to a viewing of the documentary film *Searching for Skylab* in 2023. Panel participants (L to R): Dwight Steven-Boniecki (the film's director), Jack Lousma, Rusty Schweickart, and Herb

The *Searching for Skylab* team (L to R): Carl Alessi, Dwight Steven-Boniecki, Alexandra Steven-Boniecki, Brian Fiore, Herb, and Emily Carney

Herb Baker

ALYENE BAKER

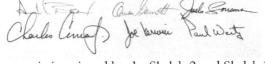

In recognition of your personal commitment to excellence in the many critical tasks that make the first Skylab mission possible.

Note of appreciation signed by the Skylab 2 and Skylab 3 crews presented to Herb's mother, Alyene Baker, for her work on the Skylab Parasol

This flag was flown aboard the third flight of the Space Shuttle "Columbia" as it completed 130 revolutions of the Earth and travelled 3.4 million miles. It is presented to you in recognition of the significant contribution you made to the success of the mission.

Presented to

HERBERT H. BAKER, JR.

Astronaut Jack R. Lousma

Administrator, National Aeronautics and Space Administration

Astronaut C. Gordon Fullerton

U.S. flag flown on *Columbia*'s STS-3 mission presented to Herb

164

An exterior view of the Shuttle Mission Simulator-Motion Base in Building 5 at JSC

Herb at Space Center Houston watching the Shuttle mockup *Independence* being mated with the Shuttle Carrier Aircraft by cranes in 2014

Herb at the B-2 Engine Test Stand at Stennis Space Center where
the hot fire tests of the core stage for the Space Launch System
rocket was conducted

Herb with NASA colleague Kristi Fryer talking with divers at the
Neutral Buoyancy Laboratory

HUMANS of JSC

ALL   COMMERCIAL CREW   EXPLORATION   HUMAN RESEARCH PROGRAM   INTERNATIONAL SPACE STATION   ORION

I have worked at Johnson Space Center more than 41 years, both in the Shuttle and International Space Station programs multiple times, among others. Over the past eight years, I supported the Flight Operations Directorate (FOD). Working so closely with FOD, I was allowed access to the Mission Control Center, the Space Vehicle Mockup Facility and the deck at the Neutral Buoyancy Lab. As a result, I'm asked to do a lot of tours here.
- Herb Baker

It is a challenge and a privilege to apply my food science expertise to feeding astronauts in microgravity and I have found it to be very fascinating and rewarding to make this contribution to the space program. As a scientist, I feel like I'm making a contribution to a very unique application and aspect of science...space exploration. It's important to me that I'm a part of a scientific endeavor that is lasting and ongoing, the human exploration of space.
- Vickie Kloeris

"Humans of JSC" article in the JSC Roundup publication profiling Herb and Vickie Kloeris, the ISS food system manager. The "Humans of JSC" feature was started by Ellen Ochoa to feature mission support employees

Herb with NASA Administrator Jim Bridenstine during the Artemis NASA Social event at the Michoud Assembly Facility in New Orleans in 2019

Chris Hadfield and Alan Bean at a luncheon/book signing in Houston attended by Herb in 2013. Walt Cunningham was also in attendance

Herb with Anna Fisher in 2017, shortly after attending a NASA retirement seminar together. Herb retired in January 2017 and Anna retired 3 months later in April 2017

Herb with Bill McArthur, whose Safety & Mission Assurance Office he worked closely with for several years

Herb with Clay Anderson, whose first book *The Ordinary Spaceman* is a favorite

Herb with Mike Massimino, who flew two Shuttle missions to the Hubble Space telescope to make repairs and who has made several appearances on the TV show *The Big Bang Theory*

Herb with Doug "Wheels" Wheelock, who is currently working with NASA to test the Orion spacecraft systems. Doug jokes that occasionally someone gets his nickname wrong and calls him "Tires"

Herb assisting Nicole Stott at the astronaut autograph show during the Astronaut Scholarship Foundation's Space Rendezvous event at the Lone Star Flight Museum near JSC in 2018

Herb with Ellen Ochoa at an Astronaut Scholarship Foundation Gala dinner at Space Center Houston in 2018

Herb with Kate Rubins, wearing her NASA Space Flight Medal,
awarded after returning from ISS Expedition 48-49, during which
she became the first person to sequence DNA in space

Herb with British ESA astronaut Tim Peake, wearing his NASA
Space Flight Medal, awarded after returning from Expedition 46-47

Tracy Caldwell Dyson, serving as Capcom, waving to Herb and the group he was touring through Mission Control at JSC

Jessica Meir waving to Herb and a group he was touring through the Neutral Buoyancy Laboratory. Jessica and Mike Barratt, still wearing their Liquid Cooling and Ventilation Garments, had just completed a spacewalk training session

Herb with Jasmin Moghbeli, who was the commander of the
SpaceX Crew-7 mission on her first space flight in 2023

Herb with Joe Acaba, Chief of the Astronaut Office, and the first
person of Puerto Rican descent to become a NASA astronaut

19 - Back to NASA Headquarters

I didn't realize it at the time, but getting out of the Space Station Program when I did was fortunate. As much as I enjoyed working with Grumman and having a short commute to my office in Reston, I could not turn down a promotion and a return to a supervisory position, even though it meant a longer commute to the Headquarters offices in downtown D.C.

Because I could commute to downtown D.C. by bus and subway in less than an hour each way, I never considered making the 25-mile trip by car. The subway I took stopped across the street from my office building, and the combined bus and subway fare to and from D.C. was only about $5 per day at the time. I usually read the Washington Post on my morning trip to D.C. and switched to USA Today for the return to Reston in the afternoon.

Beginning in 1961, NASA Headquarters occupied part of two buildings in D.C.: FOB–6 at 800 Independence Ave. SW and FOB–10 at 600 Independence Ave. SW. NASA also occupied part of the Reporters Building at 300 7th Street SW and moved into additional office space in L'Enfant Plaza, near FOB–6 and FOB–10 in the late 1980s.

My office was located at L'Enfant Plaza when I moved downtown. L'Enfant Plaza (named after Pierre L'Enfant, an American-French military engineer who designed the city layout for Washington, D.C.) is a stop on the subway. I could exit the subway car and enter my office area without having to go outdoors, which was an advantage during bad weather.

Admiral Evans was still the Assistant Administrator for Procurement. I was assigned to the Procurement Management Division, and my director was Foster Fournier. His deputy was Scott Thompson. I enjoyed working for both of them and established a valued relationship with Scott, which would come in handy several years later.

My primary responsibilities were managing NASA's procurement data system and providing information technology (IT) support. Every Federal agency is required to submit detailed data on all acquisitions above the micro-purchase threshold (made with a credit card) regularly to the Federal Procurement Data System (FPDS)—the central database for Government contracting transactions.

The data is used by the president, Congress, the Government Accountability Office (GAO), and Government agencies to make policy decisions and report on procurement trends. I had a staff of three handling data input and running database queries to answer the numerous information requests we received from NASA offices, industry, and government agencies about what NASA was buying and from which companies.

I was also responsible for producing NASA's Annual Procurement Report, which provided detailed information on NASA's procurements over the previous Government fiscal year. The data broke down the total dollars spent by NASA centers, companies receiving the awards, locations (states), levels of competition, types of contracts, types of businesses, types of products or services purchased, and many other categories.

I had a staff of two computer specialists to handle all IT support for the Headquarters Office of Procurement. They served as the IT help desk for our organization. By this time in 1988, every NASA employee had a desktop computer.

One of my "other duties as assigned" was to participate occasionally in Procurement Management Survey Teams. A team of six to eight procurement professionals from our office would spend two weeks at one of the eleven center procurement offices, reviewing their work for compliance with policies and regulations, and interviewing employees to assess their knowledge and morale. We typically visited a center once every two years. The team would write a final report documenting our findings and recommendations and share it with management at the center. The center was required to provide a written response to our report and our recommendations.

I participated in at least nine center procurement surveys—at Kennedy, Marshall, Stennis, Glenn, Langley, Ames, Goddard, JPL, and the White Sands Test Facility. One day during the survey I participated in at Marshall, Carl Eichenlaub, the head of the team, was standing in front of an awe-inspiring exhibition displaying the universe, with hundreds of lights (representing stars) twinkling in the simulated dark vastness of space. One of our survey team members walked up to Carl, who seemed entranced by the display, and whispered, "Well, that puts your freaking little survey report in perspective, doesn't it, Carl?"

* * *

In 1991, Admiral Evans retired as AA for Procurement after serving for 15 years in that job and was replaced by Darleen Druyun, who would hold the position for only two years. After leaving NASA, Druyun became the Principal Deputy Undersecretary of the Air Force for Acquisition and later pleaded guilty to a felony—violations of the conflict of interest statutes—and spent nine months in prison. After leaving the Air Force in 2003, she had taken a job with Boeing and later confessed to giving Boeing preferential treatment in numerous competitive contracts while she was with the Air Force.

Druyun admitted that she improperly awarded a multibillion-dollar contract to Boeing to upgrade the avionics on one of its military aircraft. She also paid Boeing an excessive price for upgrades to another military aircraft. She admitted to providing a competitor's bidding information to Boeing. As part of the quid-pro-quo, she negotiated a position for herself with Boeing with a huge salary and signing bonus while she was still working for the Air Force. At her request, Boeing also hired her daughter and son-in-law.

In October 2004, she was sentenced to nine months in federal prison for corruption. Boeing's CFO, Michael Sears, was fired and Boeing's CEO, Phil Condit, resigned. Boeing also paid a $615 million fine.

* * *

Druyun was replaced at NASA by Deidre "Dee" Lee. Dee had previously been married to astronaut Mark Lee. Mark later secretly married fellow astronaut Jan Davis while they were training together for the STS-47 mission. Mark Lee and Davis eventually disclosed the marriage to NASA but it was too late to make a crew substitution. On Shuttle *Endeavour* in 1992, they became the only married couple to fly together in space. NASA subsequently changed its policy to forbid married couples from flying together.

The reasons given for this policy are twofold: crew balance and children. NASA believes each crew member should interact equally with others and that couples might disrupt this balance. Also, if the couple has children, NASA doesn't want both parents on the same flight in case of an accident.

* * *

In 1992, all of NASA Headquarters was, for the first time, consolidated into one new building at 300 E Street SW, where it remains today. (In 2020, the building was named after Mary W. Jackson, one of the Black women mathematicians from the movie *Hidden Figures*.) Around the same time, I was promoted to a Senior Procurement Analyst position in the Program Operations Division. In this position, I primarily supported the procurement operations at the centers and reviewed and processed documents the centers submitted to Headquarters for approval.

* * *

One of the most important elements of a support contract is the Statement of Work, which details the work that the contractor is required to perform. I was tasked with updating and revising NASA's Statement of Work Handbook. Once I completed that, I was asked to teach the "How to Write a Statement of Work" segment of NASA's Program/Project Management training course for NASA engineers held at Wallops Flight Facility two or three times a year. It's a reasonably easy drive from the D.C. area to Wallops on Virginia's Eastern Shore, and it was usually a nice break from my other duties, so I enjoyed teaching that course for several years.

While working at Headquarters, I visited every NASA center at least once, including the White Sands Test Facility in Las Cruces, NM, and the Wallops Flight Facility. It gave me a much broader perspective of the whole Agency. It also opened my eyes to the fact that most employees at Headquarters and other centers considered JSC to be arrogant. JSC was, after all, home to the astronauts, Mission Control, and the Space Shuttle and Space Station Program Offices. Other than possibly the Kennedy Space Center, where all of the launches occurred, it also received the most national attention. If JSC was arrogant, it was something I never observed or noticed during the 30 years that I worked there, but I was obviously biased.

* * *

The most unusual Shuttle launch delay happened with STS-70 in 1995. The STS-70 Shuttle stack had been rolled out in May, with a planned launch in June. It was eventually delayed until July 13 because the external tank was attacked by a woodpecker. NASA engineers were surprised to find numerous holes and claw marks on the foam insulation of the external tank. Crew member Don Thomas thought it was a joke when he was told that their launch would be delayed because of a woodpecker.

KSC is located on Merritt Island, which is a National Wildlife Refuge and home to hundreds of different kinds of animals. Twenty-one of them are listed as endangered, and among them is a migratory woodpecker, the northern flicker. During that spring of 1995, an apparently lovesick northern flicker, during mating season, tried to make a new home for itself on the Shuttle's external tank after apparently mistaking it for a tree.

The foam on the external tank was two to three inches thick, and woodpeckers like to make nests eight to ten inches deep. This woodpecker would start pecking the foam, and when it hit the aluminum tank, being unable to go any further, would move over a few inches and start pecking the foam again, making another hole. The woodpecker ended up making at least 70 round holes in the foam insulation before the holes were noticed.

NASA attempted to patch the holes with the Shuttle still on the launch pad, but after a week without success, it decided to roll the vehicle back to the VAB for repairs. The work was completed in about one week and the vehicle was rolled back to the pad. But NASA still had a problem: how would they prevent the woodpeckers from coming back and doing the same thing again?

Air horns were used to scare woodpeckers from further attacks during the work week, but fewer personnel were there over the weekend to keep the woodpeckers away from the Shuttle. A few employees stood at different levels on the launch pad over the weekend and would blow the air horns if they saw a woodpecker. The employees were given T-shirts emblazoned with the words "Pecker Patrol."

Damage to STS-70 external tank caused by woodpecker [NASA photo]

Once this made the news, people from around the world sent suggestions to NASA on how to solve their problem. One thing NASA did was put several two-foot-high plastic owls around the pad because owls are natural enemies of woodpeckers. They also hung several beach-ball-sized balloons, called predator eyes, that had large eyes, similar to the eyes of owls and hawks, on them to scare away the woodpeckers. The solutions worked, since the woodpeckers did not return.

Once the STS-70 crew returned home after a successful flight, NASA formed a special team called the BIRD team, using the acronym for Bird Investigation Review and Deterrent Team. The team's objective was to determine what happened, why it happened, and how to prevent it from happening again.

The team believed this was most likely a lovesick woodpecker whose natural habitat around the pad had been disturbed by workers during the bird's mating season. This had driven the bird to consider the external tank as a possible new home. It was the only time an incident like this happened.

* * *

Having grown up in Houston, I do not mind the heat. I prefer the climate in Houston to that of northern Virginia, where I did not enjoy dealing with the cold, snow, and ice during winter. In January 1996, a severe snowstorm hit the area where I lived. Through the weekend of January 6 through January 8, over two feet of snow fell at Dulles Airport, just a few miles from my home.

Even more snow fell the following week, with most schools and businesses having to close. All major highways were closed on January 7, and the Metro (subway) trains were shut down through January 9. Federal and local government offices were closed. A total of two to three feet of snow on the ground and on building roofs caused three roof collapses.

I recall struggling to remove at least some of the snow that had collected on my roof after hearing about the roof collapses. The snowdrifts were several feet high in my driveway and front yard, so I was unable to travel by car. NASA was closed for the entire following week.

One day during the week, I was shoveling snow and fell after slipping on a patch of ice. I thought to myself, "What the (hell) am I doing here?" Eight months later I would be back in Houston.

* * *

Dan Goldin was appointed NASA administrator in April 1992, with a directive to cut costs. It wasn't just NASA. The entire Federal Government was undergoing a workforce reduction. Congress passed the Federal Workforce Restructuring Act, requiring the reduction of over 270,000 employees by 1999. NASA was already reducing its workforce of approximately 24,000 employees and planned to reduce it to about 17,500 by the year 2000. To reach that staffing level, NASA was expected to implement a reduction in force (RIF) to meet the goal for fiscal year 2000.

A RIF is a complicated process for abolishing positions, where employees are either released or retained in their current position or reassigned to another position based on factors like veterans' preference, length of service, and performance ratings.

The pressure to reduce staff at Headquarters was even greater than at the centers. I recall Dee Lee, our AA for Procurement at the time, holding a staff meeting to address the issue and hearing her say, "If there's a NASA center you would like to transfer to and they have a position for you, I suggest that you go." That was all I needed to hear.

Having enjoyed my earlier years at JSC and hoping to get away from winters with ice and snow, I began planning my escape from NASA Headquarters back to JSC. I contacted Robbie LaBrier, one of my friends that had worked in my Center Operations Office 12 years earlier, who was now a manager within the JSC Procurement Office, to let him know I was interested in returning to Houston.

Scott Thompson, with whom I had developed a strong working relationship at Headquarters when I first moved downtown eight years earlier, was now the Director of Procurement at JSC. Robbie spoke with Scott to let him know of my interest. Robbie hoped Scott would bring me back to JSC to work in his office.

Scott agreed to bring me back to JSC. However, rather than assigning me to the office Robbie was managing, he assigned me to the business office in the Space Station Program Office, which had been relocated from Reston to Houston several years earlier. I happily accepted the offer, and by September, I was working at JSC, with a home just three miles from the house where I had grown up in the 1960s. It was nice to be home.

20 - Back to Space Station at JSC

I was happy to be back at JSC, reunited with old friends, both at NASA and in the community, and working in a Program once again. In addition to JSC being home to the astronauts, Mission Control, and the Space Shuttle and Space Station Program Offices, there were many other aspects that I enjoyed about working there.

Herd of deer roaming the JSC campus – a fairly common occurrence

The main part of the JSC campus is beautiful, with many trees, ponds with fish (koi), deer freely roaming the grounds, and other wildlife, like squirrels and ducks. I would occasionally see an armadillo. There's even a breeding facility for endangered Attwater Prairie Chickens on JSC's grounds, a project with the Houston Zoo. There are bike racks with plenty of "free-roaming" bikes at several buildings available to any employee for riding to another building if they aren't in the mood to walk or drive.

As a University of Texas at Austin alum, one of my favorite features of JSC is the Longhorn Project—an educational program created in conjunction with the local school district, the Houston Rodeo, and the Texas Longhorn Breeders Association. George Abbey, JSC Director from 1996 to 2001, led JSC and the other groups to develop this unique facility for enhancing agricultural education.

The Longhorn Project occupies 53 acres at JSC and includes 35 acres of pasture for grazing, and a large garden area. There is a small herd of longhorns that lives at JSC and another herd on loan from the Texas Longhorn Breeders Association.

View of the Longhorn Project with Space Center Houston in the background

The Longhorn Project is situated in a section of JSC near Space Center Houston. A few years ago, I managed to get a perfectly framed photo of one of the longhorns, with its huge set of horns, resting on the ground, with the mockup Shuttle Independence sitting atop the Shuttle Carrier Aircraft at Space Center Houston in the background. Only in Houston can you take a photo like this.

* * *

Another wonderful area of JSC, also created by George Abbey, is the Astronaut Memorial Grove, where a tree with a plaque has been dedicated to astronauts who have passed away. The grove was started in 1996, when seven trees were planted in memory of the seven *Challenger* crew members who perished in the 1986 accident.

Tree dedication ceremonies are now held in honor of every astronaut who has passed away. While the grove is visible from NASA Parkway, which runs in front of JSC, the grove is not open to the public. JSC holds a Day of Remembrance ceremony every year on the last Thursday in January to honor the crew members that perished in the Apollo 1 fire, the *Challenger* accident, and the *Columbia* accident. I have attended numerous tree dedications since the grove was established.

* * *

Christina Koch and Jessica Meir at the Astronaut Memorial Grove Tree Dedication Ceremony for Walt Cunningham at JSC in 2023

I attended the tree dedication for Apollo 7 astronaut Walt Cunningham on October 19, 2023, where I found myself standing next to Jessica Meir. She was telling me about her seven-month-old baby daughter when Christina Koch joined us. By coincidence, the previous day was the fourth anniversary of their first all-female spacewalk together, so we reminisced about that historic event.

I also talked with Gene Kranz and Clay Anderson at the tree dedication that morning. I spoke with Gene about his new book, *Tough and Competent*, which had been recently released. Clay was in town from Ashland, NE, where he had recently moved to take the job as president and CEO of the Strategic Air Command & Aerospace Museum.

* * *

I once heard Clay Anderson answer the question: "What was it like to live and work in space?" He replied, "I was Superman every day: I flew to breakfast, I flew to work, and I even flew to the bathroom. I was faster than a speeding bullet [he was traveling 17,500 mph while on the Shuttle and Station]. I was more powerful than a locomotive. I could lift anything on board the Station with just two fingers. I was able to leap tall buildings in a single bound [OK, there were no tall buildings to leap over in space]. And hopefully, I stood for truth, justice, and the American way." It's hard to argue with that. He just needed crewmates named Lois Lane and Jimmy Olsen.

* * *

Every December, during the Christmas holiday season, JSC wraps lights around all of the trees in the Memorial Grove. All of the tree lights are white except for those on two trees: Pete Conrad's and Alan Bean's. Until Bean's tree dedication in 2019, Pete Conrad's tree, with red lights, stood out as the only tree that wasn't decorated with white lights. That was done in honor of Conrad's famous quote: "If you can't be good, be colorful." Pete was both—good and colorful.

There's a great story behind the Conrad and Bean trees being the only trees wrapped in colored lights during the holidays. I have enjoyed getting to know Alan's widow, Leslie Bean, over the past few years. This story is best told by Leslie in her own words:

"The story of Alan Bean's talk at Pete Conrad's Tree Planting, and Alan's 'visit' from Pete the night before the ceremony has become a bit of a NASA family legend. A few have even tried to claim that they were who did this, but it was, and could only have been, Alan Bean, Pete's teammate, and best friend.

This is how Pete's tree came to be the only tree in the Astronaut Memorial Grove at JSC in Houston that is lit in color during the holidays.

I always smile to think back on that day. It was one of the great moments. Alan had a twinkle in his eye, and a true 'Dick Gordon sparkle' about him.

When Alan told everyone at the tree planting ceremony that Pete was there, communicating with him, instructing him on what to say, people didn't know what to think. They looked around at each other, initially stunned—maybe even a little worried.

Alan began,

'Well, I sure wasn't expecting to see Pete last night, but he appeared at the foot of our bed, and he said to me,' 'Hey Al—It's me, Pete... I know you're gonna be at my Tree Dedication tomorrow, and you're worried about what you're gonna say… So, let me tell ya—when it comes your turn to talk, just stand there and hold on a few seconds—I'll tell you what to say. I've got some things to say to George Abbey.'

Now Alan stood very still, and quietly looked up and to the left. People began looking around at each other, not yet sure what was going on, or how to react.

'Okay, Pete,' Alan said, 'I understand what you want. I'll tell George just like you said.'

Alan turned to George Abbey and said, 'George, Pete says he was always the shortest guy in the office, and he doesn't want to have the shortest tree here.'

People were beginning to get into it now, and were smiling and nodding at each other, especially at Pete instructing George on what he wanted him to do.

Alan looked over at Pete's tree, paused, looked up, and said, 'Pete, I'm lookin' at your tree right now, and it's the newest one, but it's not the smallest!'

Again, Alan paused, and looked up to Pete, 'Okay Pete, I'll tell George that, too…'

People began to chuckle, and to move forward to not miss anything.

'George, Pete says for me to tell you to NOT give him a tree with those plain little white lights like everybody else's trees.'

'Pete says, 'I was a little guy, and you know I always said, if you can't be good, be colorful, and you know, I was colorful!'

Again, Alan looked up toward Pete, listening…'What'd you say, Pete? You want me to tell

George Abbey that, too? Okay, okay, Pete - I'll tell him.'

Alan looked directly at George Abbey. Now, George was laughing, too.

'George, Pete wants me to tell you he wants colorful lights on his tree. Pete wants LOTS of colorful lights on his tree. Pete wants to be sure you're gonna do that.'

By now, people were really into it, looking between Alan, and George, and at the place above Alan where he was getting directions from Pete. There was much laughter, and George promised that Pete's tree would always stand out and be colorful.

Pete's fun, colorful spirit was honored in the most delightful, creative, and loving way by his best friend.

No one else could have done it the way Alan did that day. He had everyone participating in the fun. It was great!

Everyone loved it. Everyone was having fun. The smiles and giggles continued through the ceremony.

Pete's bright red tree is now one of the traditions during the holidays at JSC. Each Christmas until 2019, Pete's tree was the only one covered in color.

In April 2019, at Alan's Tree Dedication ceremony, I told the story of that day, from Pete's ceremony in 1999. Like Alan asked George Abbey, I asked Mark Geyer, the director of JSC, if there might be one more tree decked with color each year. As the Astronaut Artist, who helped the world see the Moon in vibrant blue, violet, pink, and red, Alan's tree will reflect his love of the Moon and of color. They found the perfect spot for Alan's tree not too far from Pete's. Actually, it's about the same distance apart as their respective graves are at Arlington.

Thank you, George Abbey.

Thank you, Mark Geyer.

Thank you, Pete.

Thank you, Alan.

I'll see you later, my love.

Leslie"

* * *

I've also become acquainted with Alan's first wife, Sue, and their daughter, Amy, after meeting them at a space-themed event in 2018. Alan, Sue, and Amy were all fellow University of Texas alumni. Sue was a cheerleader at UT in 1954 and performed in gymnastics, where she met Alan, who was on the UT gymnastics team. Sue told me that she and Alan gave up gymnastics as they approached their senior year to focus on graduation, noting that gymnastics is a sport you must practice every day to stay at the top of your game. She told me that, years later, when she watched Alan doing front flips and a backflip in the weightless environment of Skylab, "I caught myself seeing perfection in space."

* * *

As mentioned earlier, Robbie LaBrier had helped me arrange my return to JSC. And now, another friend I had worked with previously, Larry Kenyon, was the deputy manager of the Space Station Business Office that I had been assigned to. The manager of the office was a woman named Lucy Yates, who had joined JSC two years after I left to work at KSC, so I wasn't previously acquainted with her.

I had been back at JSC for a short time and needed to speak to Lucy one day so I went to her office. Her door was closed, and her secretary told me, "She's in there with her father. They've been together for a while, so she'll probably be available shortly if you'd like to wait." I waited for a few minutes.

When the door opened, Gene Kranz, who had retired from NASA two years earlier, walked out of Lucy's office. I'm sure my eyes widened, and my jaw dropped as he walked past me on his way out. I stepped into Lucy's office and said, "Wait a minute! Gene Kranz is your father? Why did no one tell me this?" I must have been the only person in the building who didn't know—Yates was Lucy's married name.

* * *

Our Space Station Program Office was located in Building 4 South (4S), the same building as the Astronaut Office. The astronaut offices were on the fifth and sixth floors of the six-story building, which was just a few steps from the main cafeteria at JSC. It was a common occurrence to bump into an astronaut in the building lobby or elevators, or to see them in the cafeteria.

Even though we were adjacent to the cafeteria, which operated only for a few hours in the morning and a few hours mid-day, Building 4S also had a snack bar on the first floor, which was open all day, from 7 a.m. to 4:30 p.m., and offered snacks like freshly-baked cookies and popcorn in the afternoons.

The cookies sold for 35 cents each or three for $1. I rationalized that it was important for me to buy three cookies so I could save a nickel every time I bought them, which I did frequently.

Another cool thing about working in Building 4S was that after every Shuttle mission, the walls lining the hallway that was used to enter the building from the parking lot would be covered with "Welcome Home" banners and photos of highlights from the mission.

* * *

The Space Station Program Manager at that time was Randy Brinkley, who had a 25-year career with the Marine Corps and two years with McDonnell Douglas before joining NASA in 1992 as a special assistant in the Office of Space Flight. In January 1994, NASA Administrator Dan Goldin had asked Brinkley to become the Program Manager for the Space Station Program. At the time, the Space Station Program was transitioning from Space Station Freedom to the International Space Station.

By 1996, many of the contractor engineers involved in designing and building the Mercury, Gemini, Apollo, and Space Shuttle spacecraft had retired. JSC director George Abbey paid close attention to the Station Program, holding regular Saturday morning meetings with Space Station managers to follow the progress of their work.

These meetings were known as the George Abbey Saturday Review, or GASR (nicknamed "Gasser"). He also instituted a monthly meeting known as the Station Development and Operation Meeting (SDOM). These meetings were held at a different site each month at either one of the contractor facilities or at JSC, KSC, or Marshall Space Flight Center. The meetings were attended by senior contractor executives and the respective center director.

* * *

In 1997, I was the Lead for the International Program team in the Space Station Business Office. One of the tasks I was involved with was the acquisition of the Super Guppy aircraft, which NASA still flies today. In the summer of that year, NASA was slightly more than a year away from launching the first U.S. element of the ISS, the Unity module (also known as Node 1), from KSC.

Other large ISS elements were also being built, and NASA needed a safe and efficient way to transport those large elements from their construction sites to KSC for launch aboard the Shuttle.

Shipping cargo of that size was difficult over the roadways due to limitations caused by tunnels, low bridges, and narrow roads. Shipment by barge to KSC from sites in the west would require a trip through the Panama Canal.

Herb with the Super Guppy at Ellington Field

The only aircraft capable of transporting the ISS's large and delicate structures was the Super Guppy, a specialized aircraft with a hinged nose that opens 110 degrees and has a huge cargo area. The cargo area is 25 feet high, 25 feet wide, and 111 feet long. It has been called both the world's "most awkward" and the "fattest" airplane.

Airbus, which operated the Super Guppies, had one available, and the European Space Agency (ESA) needed Shuttle services to fly their payloads on future Shuttle flights, so we arranged a three-way barter between NASA, ESA, and Airbus. ESA paid Airbus the negotiated price, NASA agreed to provide Shuttle services for approximately 990 pounds of payload upmass (payload mass launched to orbit), and Airbus transferred the Super Guppy to NASA. This arrangement allowed ESA to spend a fixed amount in Europe instead of making payments to NASA for Shuttle services. The Super Guppy transported elements such as the Joint Airlock Module and truss segments (parts of the Station's backbone) to KSC for launch. The barter agreement was a win for all three parties.

* * *

In January 1998, NASA announced that Senator John Glenn had been selected as a payload specialist for the STS-95 crew, which would fly later that year. At age 77, he would become the oldest person to orbit Earth. He would also become the only astronaut to fly in both the Mercury and Space Shuttle programs.

* * *

Glenn was announced as one of the original Mercury Seven astronauts in 1959, and a few weeks later, the seven astronauts gathered at Cape Canaveral in Florida to watch a rocket launch for the first time. The Atlas rocket was similar to the one that would be used to carry them into orbit in the 1960s. Shortly after liftoff, the Atlas rocket exploded, shocking the astronauts. Alan Shepard turned to Glenn and said, "Well, I'm glad they got that out of the way."

It's believed that the reason Glenn didn't fly again after his Mercury Friendship 7 flight in 1962 was that President Kennedy considered Glenn a national treasure and too valuable to risk on a future spaceflight. Kennedy believed that if the first American to orbit Earth died, it would be a significant setback for the space program. Glenn retired from NASA in January 1964 at age 42.

* * *

In 1998, when Glenn reported to JSC to train for his STS-95 mission, my office was still in Building 4S, where Glenn's office would also be. I saw him only a few times, as he was a U.S. Senator at the time and made frequent trips to Washington, D.C., that year.

John Glenn speaking at the STS-95 Welcome Home at Ellington Field

The STS-95 flight was successfully completed in November 1998, and I attended the "Welcome Home" ceremony for the crew, held in a hangar at Ellington Field the day after they returned to Houston. Texas Senator Kay Bailey Hutchison, Houston Mayor Lee Brown, and each of the crew members gave brief speeches to the crowd.

* * *

While on the subject of Shepard and Glenn, Shepard tells the story of how he found out he would be the first American astronaut in space while the Mercury 7 astronauts were at Langley Field, Virginia (excerpted from his interview in the JSC Oral History Project):

"We had been in training for about 20 months or so, toward the end of 1960, early 1961, when we all intuitively felt that Bob Gilruth had to make a decision as to who was going to make the first flight. And, when we received word that Bob wanted to see us at 5:00 in the afternoon one day in our office, we sort of felt that perhaps he had decided. There were seven of us then in one office. We had seven desks around in the hangar at Langley Field.

Bob walked in, closed the door, and was very matter-of-fact as he said, 'Well, you know we've got to decide who's going to make the first flight, and I don't want to pinpoint publicly at this stage one individual. Within the organization I want everyone to know that we will designate the first flight and the second flight and the backup pilot, but beyond that we won't make any public decisions.

So, Shepard gets the first flight, Grissom gets the second flight, and Glenn is the backup for both of these two sub-orbital missions. Any questions?' Absolute silence. He said, 'Thank you very much. Good luck.'" He turned around, and left the room.

Well, there I am looking at six faces looking at me and feeling, of course, totally elated that I had won the competition. But yet almost immediately afterwards feeling sorry for my buddies, because there they were. I mean, they were trying just as hard as I was and it was a very poignant moment because they all came over, shook my hand, and pretty soon I was the only guy left in the room."

* * *

One of the most challenging responsibilities I had in my career was during this period. It involved settling a financial dispute with Boeing under the ISS prime contract. The issue had been ongoing since the contract was awarded four years earlier and involved relatively mundane issues regarding accounting principles and standards for Government contracts.

The issue was that Boeing was treating subcontractor costs in a way that increased charges to NASA by millions of dollars, with NASA receiving no benefit from those higher costs. Boeing was including those increased costs in the invoices being sent to NASA, but NASA was withholding payment for those excess costs, claiming that the costs were unreasonable as Boeing was not in compliance with their disclosed accounting practices by treating their subcontractor costs in that manner. In response, Boeing filed a claim with the Armed Services Board of Contract Appeals (ASBCA).

For a number of reasons, it was NASA's preference to resolve the issue through negotiation rather than through litigation. The primary reason was that the litigation risk was considered "high" by our NASA legal counsel for this case. In a worst-case litigation scenario, the ASBCA judge could rule in favor of Boeing and NASA could be liable, depending on when the judge made the ruling, for approximately $80 to $90 million in costs (which were being withheld by NASA) plus an additional $10 million in interest.

Additional benefits of reaching a negotiated resolution rather than through litigation included:

- Quantifying the ISS Program's funding liabilities by settling the dispute

- Avoiding degradation of NASA-Boeing teaming on the ISS Program

- Avoiding the expenditure of significant resources required to conduct litigation (interrogatories, depositions, testifying in court) for legal, business, and Space Station Program personnel

- The ability to control the outcome of negotiations as opposed to having to accept a judge's decision

Additionally, NASA believed there were no legal principles at stake that were worth fighting for at any cost. This was strictly a business issue.

Settling the issue required coordination with both the Defense Contract Audit Agency (DCAA) and the Defense Contract Management Agency (DCMA). I made several trips to Boeing's headquarters near Seattle, Washington, starting in April 1998, to meet with DCAA, DCMA, and Boeing representatives. Boeing submitted a settlement offer in June. Before making a counter-offer, I had to get approval from the Space Station Program Manager, the JSC center director, and the Associate Administrator for Space Flight at NASA Headquarters.

After a month of negotiations, Boeing agreed to make accounting changes starting in 1999 that would reduce subcontractor costs and they would also accept a management challenge to reduce prospective ISS contract costs by over $14 million. In consideration of those settlement items offered by

Boeing, NASA agreed to pay approximately $48 million in previously withheld contract costs.

A handshake agreement was reached in July, and the parties canceled a series of depositions of Boeing employees by government lawyers that had been scheduled to begin the following day. Negotiations continued for another month to resolve additional details until a final settlement was reached. I signed the contract modification that formalized the agreement in August 1998.

A few months later, I was presented with a "Center Director Certificate of Commendation" by George Abbey and astronaut Charlie Bolden for completing that project.

Herb receiving a Certificate of Commendation from JSC Director George Abbey and astronaut Charlie Bolden [NASA photo]

21 - Shuttle and Station Again

In January 2000, I found myself back in the Space Shuttle Program after the previous contracting officer for the Space Flight Operations Contract (SFOC), Jeff Cullen, transferred to NASA Headquarters. I later found out that the director of the Business Management Directorate, Jim Shannon, personally requested that I be moved from the Space Station Program to the Shuttle Program to fill that vacancy.

[Spoiler alert: I would spend four and a half years in this position before returning to the Space Station Program again. I sense a pattern here.]

In the mid-1990s, NASA faced budget constraints aimed at controlling program costs and operating more efficiently. The Government Performance and Results Act of 1993 required federal agencies to implement long-term strategic planning, measure program outcomes, and hold managers accountable for achieving results.

In July 1993, NASA had been directed to cut its budget. In 1994, NASA Administrator Dan Goldin established an independent review team to investigate ways the Shuttle program could cut costs. Their report was issued in February 1995. The team was chaired by Dr. Chris Kraft and included retired astronaut Frank Borman, along with four aerospace industry executives. The report, also known as the Kraft Report, recommended that NASA delegate most of the responsibility for operating the Shuttle to a single prime contractor.

The resulting Space Flight Operations Contract was initially intended to be a competitive procurement. However, when two leading contenders, Rockwell and Lockheed Martin, formed a joint venture called United Space Alliance (USA) to compete together rather than against each other, NASA reconsidered its decision.

In November 1995, NASA approved a Justification for Other than Full and Open Competition (JOFOC) to contract solely with USA for the SFOC contract. The decision was based on, among other considerations, the fact that the two parent companies of USA were already providing most of the workforce supporting the Shuttle Program.

The contract award was completed in September 1996 with a value of $6.95 billion. The existing contracts supporting the Shuttle Program were consolidated under SFOC in two phases. Phase I would consolidate the 12 existing Rockwell and Lockheed Martin contracts. Phase II would consolidate an additional 15 contracts being performed by other contractors.

USA was now responsible for:

- Mission design and planning
- Software development and integration
- Astronaut & flight controller training
- System integration
- Flight operations
- Vehicle processing, launch, and recovery
- Vehicle sustaining engineering
- Flight crew equipment processing
- ISS support

NASA characterized its relationship under the new SFOC contract as shifting from insight to oversight. This meant that NASA would define the results desired (e.g., what and when) while USA would be responsible for determining "How" to meet NASA's "What and When."

In my new position, I became the lead contracting officer for the SFOC contract. Twenty years after struggling with an excessive number of contract changes that needed to be negotiated on the original Shuttle Orbiter Vehicle contract, we were now facing a similar problem with the SFOC contract—the definitization process taking too long to complete. The Government standard for undefinitized contract actions was 180 days from the issuance of a change order to definitization being completed. Many SFOC changes remained outstanding for over 300 days, with some approaching 400 days.

Our office, in conjunction with the USA Business Management office, formed the Change Process Improvement Team (CPIT) to identify ways to streamline and expedite the process. Several improvements were implemented, such as waiving the requirement for a DCAA audit on low-risk actions. The primary improvement, however, was for NASA and USA to work together to "partner" the change by agreeing on certain details before the change was formally issued.

One could argue that the process was, in today's terms, a "cheat code." The partnering process allowed much of the work normally done after issuance to be started before issuance, thereby delaying the start of the 180-day clock. That's a simplified description of the process, but it worked well initially as a pilot program and was eventually approved for full implementation on all SFOC changes.

* * *

The Extended Duration Orbiter (EDO) Pallet Mission Kit in the payload bay of a Space Shuttle Orbiter [NASA photo]

In 1996, Boeing bought Rockwell's aerospace and defense units and assumed the rights and obligations formerly held by Rockwell under the Orbiter contract. In February 2002, Boeing requested that they be allowed to remove the Rockwell logo on the Extended Duration Orbiter (EDO) Pallet Mission Kit and replace it with their Boeing corporate logo for media exposure purposes.

The EDO Pallet consisted of tanks of liquid hydrogen, liquid oxygen, and avionics boxes, and was installed in the Orbiter's payload bay. Cryogenic fluids from the pallet would feed additional cryogenic fluids to the Orbiter's electricity-generating fuel cells, allowing the mission time to be extended from 8 to 16 days.

The pallet had been designed and constructed by Rockwell. In March 1990, under the original Orbiter Vehicle contract, NASA and Rockwell had signed an agreement whereby Rockwell would initially fund the costs for designing and building the pallet and NASA would reimburse Rockwell for the full cost of the pallet, plus a fixed fee, in three yearly payments after the pallet was delivered.

Informal discussions with Boeing regarding replacing the Rockwell logo on the pallet with the Boeing logo had been ongoing for a couple of months. Boeing's arguments, in my opinion, were not supported by contractual language and went against NASA policy. I determined that USA's arguments were not persuasive, so I denied their request on multiple occasions.

Despite those denials, Boeing submitted a formal claim to NASA, arguing that it had the right to place its logo on the EDO pallet. As lead contracting officer for SFOC, I would have to review the claim and make a final decision.

It was my position that both Rockwell and NASA had satisfied their contractual obligations. Rockwell funded the design and development of the Pallet Mission Kit, then delivered it to NASA. Rockwell placed its corporate logo in a conspicuous location on the Pallet Mission Kit. NASA reimbursed Rockwell for the cost and fee as agreed. The EDO pallet first flew on Shuttle Flight STS-50 in June 1992 and flew an additional 13 times afterward.

Under a literal interpretation of the contract language, the Government's obligation regarding the logo was fully satisfied once Rockwell placed its corporate logo on the EDO Pallet. There was no indication in the contract of the government's obligation extending beyond Rockwell's initial placement of the logo in 1992.

In attempting to reach a fair and unbiased final decision on Boeing's claim, I contacted Dee Lee (my former boss at NASA Headquarters), the contracting officer who had originally executed the relevant contract modification. I asked if she had any recollection of any discussions or agreements regarding the time period during which the Contractor would be allowed to place or maintain its logo on the EDO Pallet. She could recall no such discussions. I also asked Boeing if they had any documentation supporting their claim that they had not previously provided. They were unable to provide any such documentation. Given those considerations, in July 2002, I denied Boeing's claim.

Boeing could have appealed my decision by filing a notice of appeal to the Armed Services Board of Contract Appeals or by filing suit in the U.S. Court of Federal Claims. However, the issue became moot early the following year when the EDO pallet was placed in the payload bay of *Columbia* on its STS-107 flight. The pallet was destroyed upon reentry.

* * *

On Saturday, February 1, 2003, the last thing on my mind was that EDO pallet. We lost all seven crew members that morning as Shuttle *Columbia* broke apart in the skies above East Texas, just minutes before it was scheduled to land at Kennedy Space Center.

I was at home listening to the news and getting a sick feeling, remembering the *Challenger* accident almost exactly 17 years earlier. I was not part of the *Columbia* recovery effort, so I did not have to go back to work until the following Monday.

I attended the STS-107 Memorial at JSC on February 4, where President George W. Bush, NASA Administrator Sean O'Keefe, and Chief Astronaut Kent Rominger spoke.

STS-107 Memorial

National Aeronautics and Space Administration
Lyndon B. Johnson Space Center
Houston, Texas
February 4, 2003

STS-107 Memorial Service
Tuesday, February 4, 2003

539th Air Force Band of the West, Lackland Air Force Base
Musical Prelude

United States Navy Band Sea Chanters
O God, Our Help in Ages Past

Rabbi Harold Robinson, Capt., Chaplain Corps (USNR)
Invocation

United States Navy Band Sea Chanters
God of Our Fathers, Whose Almighty Hand

Sean O'Keefe
NASA Administrator

Captain Kent V. Rominger (USN)
Chief of the Astronaut Corps

United States Navy Band Sea Chanters
Eternal Father, Strong to Save

Remarks by the President of the United States

Gene Theriot, Capt., Chaplain Corps (USN)
Benediction

PN2 Stephen Escalante (USNR)
Tolling of the Bells

Fly-by with NASA T-38s
Missing Man Formation

Program from the STS-107 Memorial at JSC on February 4, 2003

* * *

NASA Administrator Sean O'Keefe established the *Columbia* Accident Investigation Board (CAIB) shortly after the *Columbia* accident. The CAIB worked in a building just outside the JSC campus. I did not have to provide any personal testimony, but I helped prepare charts presented to the Board and was asked to gather and provide numerous documents, such as copies of the SFOC contract, briefing charts on the CPIT change process, copies of contract negotiation memoranda, financial management reports, and copies of business management review presentations.

* * *

Almost all major program contracts I worked on during my career, including the SFOC contract, were award fee contracts. An award fee contract is a type of contract used in government contracting that incentivizes the contractor by providing an opportunity to earn additional fees for exceeding the government's expectations in areas such as quality, timeliness, cost control, innovation, and other performance metrics.

Award fee contracts establish a specified amount of fee dollars that may be earned based upon the contractor's performance and identifies evaluation criteria against which the contractor will be measured. At NASA, a Performance Evaluation Board, appointed for that particular contract, meets to consider the evaluation inputs and recommends a rating and numerical score to the chair of the Board, called the Fee Determination Official (FDO). The FDO does not have to accept the rating/score recommended by the Board. In my experience, if the FDO chose to raise or lower the recommended score, they would explain their rationale and discuss it with the Board until a consensus was achieved.

Throughout the contract performance, the contractor and the government would document and maintain records related to the performance evaluations, ratings, and award fee calculations. Those records serve as evidence for the award fee payments and are often subject to audits and reviews.

I referenced the details of how award fee contracts work because that particular element of the SFOC contract kept me busy on several fronts for the next several months, not only with the CAIB and Inspector General, but also on a special Board of Investigation to which I was appointed, regarding the application of the Fee Reduction for Catastrophic Loss article in the SFOC contract.

The *Columbia* accident occurred during the 13th award fee period, a 6-month period that began on October 1, 2002, and ended on March 31, 2003. The CAIB concluded that, "NASA relies very extensively on contract financial incentives to motivate major Shuttle program contractors. There is no evidence these contract provisions directly contributed to the *Columbia* accident. Nor is there evidence they actually motivate contractors and enhance excellence."

The report added, "Overall, the extensive use of contract financial incentives in the Space Shuttle Program seems more a reaction to government-wide procurement policies than something NASA managers invented as an important program management tool. The award fee structure in the SFOC seems to have been primarily the work of procurement personnel, not technical program managers." I can't argue with that observation.

Between October 2003 and February 2004, after the CAIB report was released, the OIG performed an in-depth review of all 12 prior award fee evaluation periods for the SFOC contract. The OIG report issued in March 2004 stated, "We are unable to reach a conclusion on whether the fee structure of the SFOC was conducive to safe Shuttle operations."

* * *

In late 2003, I participated on the Board of Investigation necessitated by the Fee Reduction for Catastrophic Loss article in the SFOC contract. The article states, "A fee reduction will be assessed in the event of loss of an Orbiter and/or individuals associated with Space Flight Operations when such loss is caused by the acts or omissions of the Contractor in performance of effort under this contract." The article also states, "In the event of loss, the Contractor will forfeit all fee earned or available during the six-month award fee evaluation period in which the loss occurs. The contracting officer, in conjunction with a Board of Investigation, shall make a determination as to the cause of the loss."

The Board of Investigation was appointed on October 7, 2003, by General Michael Kostelnik, the Deputy Associate Administrator for International Space Station and Space Shuttle Programs at NASA Headquarters. The members were Randy Stone, deputy director of JSC, who served as Chairman; Frank Benz, Director of Engineering at JSC; Bill Kilpatrick, Director of Engineering at MSFC; Tip Talone, Director of International Space Station/Payloads Processing at KSC; and Jennifer Aranda, attorney at JSC. I served as the contracting officer for the Board. In accordance with the contract, our task was to determine the cause of the catastrophic loss.

Our Board worked full-time for the next two weeks reviewing the CAIB report, Shuttle program requirements documents, and other reports, and conducting interviews. Our interviewees included Ron Dittemore, the Shuttle Program Manager at the time of the accident, who resigned from NASA three months afterward; Jim Costello, Shuttle Business Manager; Lambert Austin, Shuttle Systems Integration Manager; Bill Harris, Shuttle Safety and Mission Assurance Manager; and Ralph Roe, Shuttle Vehicle Engineering Office Manager; among others. We also interviewed retired astronaut Mike McCulley who had been named president and CEO of United Space Alliance in May 2003.

Our Board's report, which was never made public, was transmitted to General Kostelnik on October 24, 2003. We had reviewed the STS-112 and STS-113 missions (the two Shuttle flights immediately preceding STS-107) and determined that a cause of the *Columbia* accident was the failure to recognize the significance of the bipod foam loss on STS-112. During the STS-112 launch, the ET bipod ramp shed a chunk of foam that caused a dent 4" wide and 3" deep into the metal SRB-ET Attach Ring near the bottom of the left SRB. Prior to the next mission, STS-113, a decision was made to continue with launches as scheduled. The launch subsequent to STS-113 was STS-107.

Our Board found that USA failed to recognize and act on the increased risk to the Shuttle Program resulting from the ET bipod foam loss on STS-112. USA had failed to raise this increased concern to NASA Program management, or in formal forums designed for this purpose, such as the Systems Safety Review Panel, Program Requirements Control Board, and the STS-113 and STS-107 Flight Readiness Reviews.

SFOC requirements clearly placed responsibility and accountability on USA to assure the safety of flight and to independently take steps to evaluate all anomalies for their impact on Space Shuttle Vehicle systems. No analysis was provided to NASA to quantify the level of risk associated with foam of this size and origin, as experienced on STS-112, or whether or where it might impact the Orbiter.

Our Board concluded that USA failed to ensure the safety of both the STS-113 and STS-107 missions. USA did not provide an assessment of the risk to the Orbiter resulting from the loss of bipod foam on STS-112, nor did it make a recommendation for mitigation, as required by the SFOC contract. The Board determined that a cause of the catastrophic loss of the Orbiter vehicle and its crew was this omission by the contractor in the performance of duties under the SFOC contract and that the provisions of the Fee Reduction for Catastrophic Loss article should be invoked.

If the Fee Determination Official for SFOC, General Kostelnik, agreed with our position, it would mean that $81.2 million in fees for award fee period 13 would be forfeited by USA. However, Kostelnik took a more nuanced approach to his fee determination decision. With two successful missions (despite the foam strike on STS-112) during the same 6-month evaluation period, STS-112 in October 2002 and STS-113 in November/December 2002, and one catastrophic mission, STS-107 in January/February, there were many factors to consider in making a determination. In fact, Kostelnik made his determination without the usual evaluation and scoring input from a Performance Evaluation Board.

General Kostelnik felt that it could not be definitively determined that acts or omissions of USA were the proximate cause, let alone the sole cause, of the loss of *Columbia* and her crew. He noted, however, that the structure of the Shuttle Program created significant involvement by USA in nearly every aspect of NASA's decision-making process.

Consequently, he determined that USA acted as an integral team member of the Shuttle Program team, which reached flawed conclusions about the safety of *Columbia* and her crew before and during the flight. Given those considerations, he determined that USA would be awarded $36 million in fees out of the total available amount of $81.2 million for that period. The result was a penalty of $45.2 million, which USA management did not dispute.

With the expectation of significant media interest regarding this fee decision, a list of prepared answers to 13 anticipated questions was coordinated with USA and was distributed to those involved in the process for use by both NASA and USA personnel. Below are samples of the questions:

• Did the SFOC catastrophic loss provision apply to *Columbia's* loss?

• What was USA's award fee score for the period and how much did they earn? [Note: USA did not receive a numerical score or adjective rating for this period as they normally would have.]

- Are changes in USA leadership likely? Will anyone be fired or has anyone resigned because of this?

- Is this just a matter of USA being the scapegoat for a flawed NASA culture?

* * *

Six months after completing the STS-107 Board of Investigation activity, in May 2004, I was promoted to the position of deputy manager in the Space Station Procurement Office. I would be leaving the Shuttle Program for the last time.

It was also the sixth time in my career that I moved either from a different job or a different location to start a new position supporting the Space Station Program. I enjoyed every one of those new assignments, including this one, where I would be working with a friend, Laura Pepper, who was the manager of the office.

* * *

Construction of the ISS would, obviously, be delayed with Shuttle flights on hold. Many of the ISS components were designed precisely for the Shuttle cargo bay. Those components could not be delivered by either the European or Russian vehicles. Another cause for delay: when the Shuttle began flying again—there would be one fewer Orbiter in the fleet.

The ISS Program would also need resupply missions and transportation to and from the ISS for its astronauts. Use of the Russian Progress capsules for resupply missions and their Soyuz capsules for taxicabs/lifeboats was necessary to address those concerns.

Delivering replacement parts to the ISS and dealing with the station's decaying orbit were other issues. The Shuttles played an important role in providing boosts to the ISS, now weighing 197 tons, to keep it at the desired altitude in orbit.

The Shuttle would eventually return to flight with the successful STS-114 mission in July 2005, roughly 2 ½ years after the *Columbia* accident. There were numerous changes and improvements to the Shuttle Program and the Orbiter fleet during that break. Improvements were also made to the solid rocket boosters and the main engines.

* * *

Photo of the ISS signed by the Expedition 1 crew presented to Herb

Fast forward to early 2006—the Shuttle was flying again, the Station assembly was continuing, and the new Constellation Program was underway. Soon thereafter, the Director of Procurement at JSC, Debra Johnson, informed me that she was transferring me to the Exploration Systems Procurement Office supporting the Constellation Program. Debra did not want any of her staff to get too comfortable in any one position.

When I left the Station Program, I received a photo (now hanging on the wall of my home office) of the ISS signed by the Expedition 1 crew: Commander Bill Shepherd, Russian Yuri Gidzenko, and Russian Sergei Krikalev. They were the first crew to board the ISS on November 2, 2000, and the ISS has been continuously inhabited since that day.

22 - Constellation Program

In early 2006, I became the deputy manager of the Exploration Systems Procurement Office, working with Jose Garcia, the manager of our office. Jose would later become the Director of Procurement at JSC. The Exploration Systems Office had been established at JSC shortly after President Bush, in 2004, called for NASA to return to the Moon and eventually Mars with the new Constellation Program (abbreviated as CxP).

The Constellation Program would consist of a crew capsule called the Crew Exploration Vehicle or CEV; two launch vehicles, called Ares I and Ares V (heavy lift); and a Lunar Lander named *Altair*. Lockheed's Orion vehicle was selected competitively for future development of the CEV.

As part of supporting the Constellation Program Office, our office managed the contract awarded to Lockheed Martin for the design, development, test, evaluation, and production of Orion with an initial contract value of $3.9 billion. We also supported the new Commercial Orbital Transportation Services (COTS) program, which had been announced in January 2006. NASA established the COTS program, hoping to encourage the commercial development of space vehicles to eventually deliver both crew and cargo to the ISS.

In addition to supporting the Constellation Program Office, which was located at JSC, I supported the COTS activities, the new Lunar Lander (*Altair*) Project Office, and the new Lunar Surface Systems Project Office.

I still have unpleasant memories of a particular meeting that occurred during my first week in this office. I had to

217

present the CxP Acquisition Strategy to the Associate Administrator for the Exploration Systems Mission Directorate at NASA Headquarters, Dr. Scott "Doc" Horowitz (a former Shuttle astronaut), on a video conference call.

The purpose of the meeting was to gain Horowitz's approval for our contracting approach to support both the Constellation Program and the Orion Project. The challenge for me was that the charts and strategy I was expected to present had already been approved at JSC, but had been prepared by the person who had previously been in my position and had left. I did not have ownership of the charts, and it was too late to make changes.

Early in the presentation, one of the charts I was presenting showed that our plan was to award one contract to provide engineering support to the Constellation Program office and award a separate contract to provide similar support to the Orion Project office. Dr. Horowitz asked me why we planned to award two separate contracts at the same time when the Program/Project offices were part of the same program located at the same center. I thought about it for a moment, and the best answer I could come up with was: "Because the CxP Program Manager and the Orion Project Manager would like to have their own contracts to avoid a conflict of interest."

Horowitz was obviously annoyed as he yelled back, "Well, I'd like to have a new car, but I'm not going to get one!" Quickly recognizing that he did not agree with that approach and that this was not the ideal time for me to start an argument, I nodded my head and said, "Next chart, please." The meeting continued without further discussion on that subject.

As fate would have it, Dr. Horowitz resigned from NASA one year later, in August 2007. As we had originally planned, our office awarded an Orion Project Integration Contract

(OPIC) to Barrios Technology in December 2007 and separately awarded a Constellation Program Support Contract (CPSC) to SGT in February 2008. We won that battle, after all.

* * *

On a slightly embarrassing note, as we were beginning the acquisition process for the contract to support the Orion Project Office, I thought Project Integration Support Services would be a good name for the contract. NASA likes to give names to its contracts and often tries to create clever acronyms to match. One of my favorite acronym examples is when JSC awarded a contract for security services on-site and called it COPS, for Center Operations Protective Services.

The embarrassing story for me is that when I came up with the name Project Integration Support Services, I had not given the associated acronym any thought until the Business Development Manager for Barrios Technology, Anita Renteria, came into my office one day and asked, "You aren't really going to call it that, are you?"

It was not until that moment that I realized what a poor choice it would have been. Our eventual contract name, OPIC (Orion Project Integration Contract), was a much better name/acronym than PISS would have been.

* * *

NASA Administrator Mike Griffin stated that his plan for the COTS Program was to "utilize, to the fullest extent possible, commercially developed cargo resupply and, ultimately, crew rotation capabilities for the ISS." NASA had historically developed these capabilities in-house, but they now believed that private industry might be able to provide these services more efficiently than the Federal Government.

The announcement soliciting COTS proposals from industry was released in January 2006. Proposals were received from 21 companies by the due date. I had worked with Alan Lindenmoyer, COTS Program Manager, a few years earlier when we were both in the ISS Program. I became involved with COTS after the proposals were received during the evaluation phase.

A unique feature of this activity was the use of Space Act Agreements (SAAs) rather than traditional contracts. Government contracts are used to acquire goods and services but, in this case, the needed services (cargo and crew flights to low Earth orbit) were not available from U.S firms. COTS was intended to provide support and "seed money" that would encourage commercial U.S. companies to deliver both cargo and crew to the ISS.

Not being subject to the Federal Acquisition Regulations that contracts must follow, the Space Act Agreements provided additional flexibility, such as allowing the companies to retain maximum rights to their intellectual and personal property resulting from these agreements. Also, NASA's commitment to purchase operational services from any successful commercial company improved the ability for the companies to raise funds.

For the proposal evaluations, we evaluated business plans as well as technical approaches, since the commercial partners were required to fund over 50% of their development costs. We had a venture capitalist on our evaluation panel, which was unusual for NASA. Six finalists were selected for further evaluation: SpaceX, Rocketplane Kistler (RpK), Andrews Space, Transformational Space Corp., Spacehab, and SpaceDev.

For those six finalists, site visits were conducted, and each company made a presentation and answered NASA's questions. The evaluation panel presented its findings to the Source Selection Official, "Doc" Horowitz, who selected SpaceX and RpK for inclusion in the COTS portfolio.

NATIONAL AERONAUTICS AND
SPACE ADMINISTRATION

BY: _____
Scott Horowitz
Associate Administrator for Exploration
Systems

DATE: _8/18/2006_

SPACE EXPLORATION
TECHNOLOGIES CORP.

BY: _____
Elon Musk,
Chief Executive Officer

1310 E. Grand Avenue
El Segundo, CA 90245

DATE: _6-26-06_

Signature page from NASA's Space Act Agreement with SpaceX for Commercial Orbital Transportation Services Demonstration

In August 2006, SpaceX was awarded a funded SAA with $250 million in NASA funding, and RpK was awarded a SAA with $207 million in NASA funding. The SAAs established fixed-price performance milestones with objective criteria that had to be met to receive the allocated NASA funding.

Lindenmoyer and I conducted "feedback sessions" with each of the unsuccessful offerors so they would understand why they had not been selected for award. We intentionally referred to the meetings as "feedback sessions" to distinguish them from debriefings that would normally be required for contracts awarded under the Federal Acquisition Regulations (FAR). This precluded the unsuccessful offerors' ability to protest the awards to the Government Accountability Office (GAO), which they would have otherwise been granted under the FAR.

NASA would later terminate the agreement with RpK due to its failure to meet one of the milestones for acquiring private funding. To replace RpK in the COTS portfolio, NASA signed a Space Act Agreement with Orbital Sciences. Due to the success of COTS, NASA later awarded contracts for the delivery of cargo to the ISS to both Orbital Sciences and SpaceX under the Commercial Resupply Services (CRS) program, which is continuing successfully today.

* * *

My interactions with Ellen Ochoa, when she was the JSC director, were always professional and businesslike, but she did have a sense of humor. I heard astronaut Mark Polansky tell a story about how Ellen pranked a group of rookie astronauts on their first Shuttle flight. STS-116 launched in December 2006 with Commander Polansky and Mission Specialist 2, Robert "Beamer" Curbeam, as the only veterans on the flight. Pilot Bill Oefelein and Mission Specialists Nicholas Patrick, Christer Fuglesang (the first flight of a Scandinavian astronaut), Joan Higginbotham, and Suni Williams were all making their first flight.

The seven-member crew walked out of the astronaut crew quarters into the waiting Astrovan (a modified Airstream motorhome) for the nine-mile trip to the launch pad, where Shuttle *Discovery* awaited. Upon arrival at the launch pad, Ellen told the crew, "Good luck and have a safe trip." Then she added, with a straight face, "Just one more thing before you climb into *Discovery*. I will need to collect your boarding passes."

Polansky and Beamer, who were both in on the joke, reached into their suit pockets and pulled out their fake boarding passes, handed them to Ellen, and stepped out of the van. The five rookie crew members froze for just a second, with panicked expressions on their faces, before realizing that they had been duped.

* * *

Our office was supporting the new Constellation Lunar Lander Project Office (LLPO), managed by Lauri Hansen. The Lunar Lander was called "*Altair*," named after the twelfth-brightest star in the night sky. In February 2008, I issued a Broad Agency Announcement requesting proposals from industry for the potential award of six-month study contracts.

The LLPO had developed a minimum set of requirements for Altair and was seeking industry input in two areas: 1) design evaluation and safety improvements; and 2) ideas from commercial industry for minimizing the life cycle costs of the project.

Having lived through those awe-inspiring Apollo lunar landing missions and then, almost 40 years later, having the opportunity to participate in the early stages of developing a new lunar lander for NASA was very exciting for me. It made the cancellation of the Constellation Program a few years later especially heartbreaking when the *Altair* project did not survive.

* * *

In addition to the *Altair* project, I was supporting the Lunar Surface Systems Project Office. For six to nine months, the office had been studying various functional needs and technical challenges inherent in exploring the lunar surface and was seeking innovative concepts associated with challenges such as regolith moving, energy storage, minimum functionality habitats, consumables packaging, avionics, and software.

NASA wanted to build on the expertise gained over the previous 50 years of spaceflight by soliciting ideas and concepts from universities, aerospace, and non-aerospace companies that could be incorporated into their lunar surface systems planning.

The idea was to reach organizations not traditionally engaged with the space industry that had applicable expertise and innovative ideas. An example of this was getting Caterpillar, the world's leading manufacturer of construction and mining equipment, involved in ideas for moving regolith on the lunar surface.

In June 2008, I issued another Broad Agency Announcement requesting proposals from industry for the award of six-month study contracts in the following Lunar Surface Systems topic areas:

- Alternative Packaging Options
- Minimum Functionality Habitation Module
- Innovative Avionics Architectures & Sparing Strategies
- Long-term Lunar Energy Storage System Concepts
- Alternative Software Architecture Development Approaches
- Lunar Regolith Moving Methods & Techniques

We received 78 proposals from 53 different companies (which could submit proposals in multiple categories) that covered all six study areas. That number of proposals was an order of magnitude greater than the number of proposals I had received in response to any previous solicitation issued during my career. I was one of the four members of the evaluation panel that reviewed and rated all 78 proposals.

We had expected a large number of proposals since we were covering six different topic areas. To simplify the evaluation, our plan was to rate each proposal in one of three categories: "Highest Rated," "Good," or "Lower Rated." It was our good fortune that there was at least one proposal receiving a "Highest Rated" evaluation in all six areas, with a total of 12 proposals being in that "Highest Rated" category.

The Source Selection Official selected all 12 for the award of small study contracts. It was also our good fortune that the total dollar value of the 12 contracts matched our budget.

The hardest part of the process for me was that, once the selections for award were made, I had to personally telephone, as promptly as possible, all 41 unsuccessful companies (sending an impersonal email was inappropriate) to inform them that their proposals had not been selected for a contract award. I spent the entire day on the phone giving that unhappy news to those 41 companies.

* * *

A disturbing event occurred at JSC on April 20, 2007. A contractor employee shot and killed NASA engineer David Beverly on the grounds of JSC.

The gunman was 60-year-old William Phillips. The shooting was prompted by an email message Phillips had received from his employer, Jacobs Engineering Group, that described problems with his work and offered suggestions on improvement. Jacobs officials stated that they were not planning to fire Phillips, although he believed he was going to be fired and he blamed Beverly.

Phillips shot and killed Beverly. He also took a hostage, Fran Crenshaw, and held her captive for over three hours before committing suicide by shooting himself. The building was surrounded by SWAT teams, and all of JSC, including a nearby middle school, was placed on lockdown.

I had gone from my office in Building 17 to a meeting in Building 1 that afternoon. I was surprised when I was told I had to stay inside when I tried to leave Building 1. There were feelings of shock and disbelief when we began hearing news about the reason for the lockdown.

The incident ended around 5 p.m. after Phillips committed suicide.

* * *

I can't help but wonder what might have been if the Constellation Program had not been canceled in 2010 due to budget and schedule issues. Despite the cancellation of that Program, Orion development continued, and today's Space Launch System (SLS) replaced the Ares booster program. Orion and SLS are part of the Artemis Program.

After the *Altair* lunar lander project was canceled, NASA chose to let private industry compete with its own designs for providing the lunar lander for Artemis. That project is called the Human Landing System (HLS), and NASA has awarded contracts to both SpaceX and Blue Origin to develop their own Human Landing Systems.

* * *

While supporting the Constellation Program/Orion Project, my office was on the second floor of Building 17. Over the years, I've seen several elevators around JSC decorated with various space themes.

One of my favorites was an elevator in Building 17 that I often took on the way to my office on the second floor. The outer doors were decorated to resemble an airlock. When the doors opened, the interior was decorated as if one were walking on the Moon, with signs of habitation.

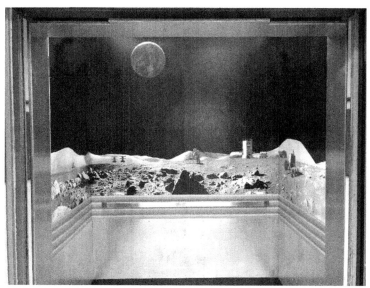

Exterior (top photo) and interior (bottom photo) of elevator in Building 17 at JSC

The windows of Building 17 facing the main road through JSC also make it clear to everyone driving by in which building the Orion Program offices are located.

Windows of Building 17 at JSC – home to the Orion Program Office

23 - Projects

In October 2008, I was moved to a new office again. This change was a shock to my system because, for the majority of my career—including the previous 12 years—I had worked in either the Shuttle Program, the Station Program, or the Constellation Program. This new position was deputy manager of the Projects Procurement Office.

Rather than being dedicated to a single program run by a program manager, this office supported several different offices, or projects, throughout JSC. Our biggest customer was the Engineering Directorate, the largest organization at JSC.

We also provided support to the Mission Operations Directorate, the Space and Life Sciences Directorate (now called Human Health & Performance), and the Astromaterials Research & Exploration Science Directorate. The procurement office located remotely at the White Sands Test Facility (WSTF) in Las Cruces, New Mexico, was also part of our office.

Six months after joining this office, I was promoted from deputy to manager, and Michelle Isermann was promoted to the deputy position I had just vacated. She and I worked well together as manager and deputy for the next three years.

* * *

There were approximately 30 people in our office, including the small group at WSTF. There was little reason to travel in this position, so it was nice to visit Las Cruces five or six times a year to oversee that group. In addition, the Site Manager for WSTF would hold a retreat every year in

Cloudcroft, NM—a small village about 90 miles east of Las Cruces—in the Sacramento Mountains of the Lincoln National Forest at an elevation of almost 9,000 feet. The retreat was always held at a place called The Lodge, which has a reputation for being haunted by a ghost.

The legend involves a young woman named Rebecca who disappeared after her lumberjack lover found her with another man. Some guests swear that Rebecca still wanders the halls of The Lodge. Guests have described ashtrays sliding across tables, doors opening and closing on their own, furniture moving, and lights turning on and off by themselves.

The belief is that Rebecca is in search of a new lover. There is at least one NASA employee I know who was at one of those retreats and witnessed something that couldn't be explained. That person left the lodge before the retreat was completed and refused to return.

* * *

In January 2010, several JSC procurement offices—including mine—moved into the third floor of a new three-story building at JSC. The new Building 20 was NASA's first LEED Platinum-certified building. The Leadership in Energy and Environmental Design (LEED) Green Building rating system is the national standard for the design, construction, and operation of high-performance green (sustainable) buildings.

The building was constructed of 30% recycled materials, reduced potable water usage by 40%, and required 57% less energy to operate than most. It also provided natural daylight to all office spaces. From my office, I could see Space Center Houston nearby without getting up from my desk. I spent most of the next seven years working in Building 20.

* * *

Herb receiving NASA's Exceptional Service Medal from Ellen Ochoa and Mike Coats

In May 2010, I was awarded the NASA Exceptional Service Medal by astronauts Mike Coats (JSC Director) and Ellen Ochoa (JSC Deputy Director) in a ceremony in the Teague Auditorium. That was a proud day for me, especially since the presentation took place in the Teague Auditorium where, 40 years earlier as a teenager, I had spent time in that same building working for the news media covering the Apollo and Skylab missions.

* * *

In November 2010, I was invited to simulate flying the Shuttle in the Shuttle Mission Simulator-Motion Base (SMS-MB) in Building 5 at JSC, which is the Mission Simulator and Training Facility. Every Shuttle crew "flew" the SMS-MB as part of their training at JSC.

It was built in 1976 to support the approach and landing tests flown by *Enterprise* off the back of the Boeing 747. (Fred Haise was one of its early users.) After modification for Orbiter flight tests, it was used for crew training for STS-1, starting in January 1979.

Herb "flying" the Shuttle SMS-MB simulator

I sat in the Shuttle commander's seat and simulated flying the Shuttle to a landing on the runway at the Shuttle Landing Facility at KSC, with guidance from a trainer who was sitting in the pilot's seat. When I stepped out of the simulator, STS-1 pilot Bob Crippen, who had trained in that same simulator 30 years earlier, was standing nearby. Someone asked him, "What brings you here, Crip? Need a refresher?" He was actually there to visit his daughter, Susan, who was a Shuttle crew trainer at JSC, working in the same building the simulator occupied at the time.

The SMS-MB was retired in 2011 after the last Shuttle mission was completed. NASA reached an agreement with Texas A&M University to use it as a teaching and engineering development tool, but the funding and logistics planned for that fell through, and the SMS-MB was put into storage. In 2016, plans were made to restore it and move it to the Lone Star Flight Museum at Ellington Field. After its restoration, the simulator was moved to its new home at the museum in April 2022, where it remains today.

* * *

In late 2011, Greg Della Longa took over the deputy position in my office. I enjoyed working with Greg. We became friends when he started at NASA in the early 1980s, but this was the first time we had worked together in the same office. We've been friends now for 40 years, and I still see him often.

* * *

During this period, I worked with Steve Altemus, the Director of Engineering at JSC, on the Morpheus Project. The goal of the project was to develop a vertical takeoff and landing test vehicle that was capable of autonomous flight.

Morpheus vehicle being prepped for test firing at JSC [NASA photo]

The project used cost- and time-saving engineering practices known as lean development. I recall one conversation with Altemus when he told me that they had been searching for the best way to incorporate baffles in Morpheus's spherical fuel tanks. Baffles are used to reduce the effect of fuel sloshing around when the vehicle is in motion. Baffles also keep fuel at the point of exit, which is especially important in reduced gravity, and prevent the fuel gauge from fluctuating.

A major aerospace company had quoted several thousand dollars to conduct a study and build the baffles for Morpheus. Not wanting to spend that much, several of JSC's student interns got together and came up with an idea for a solution. Altemus said that the students went to Home Depot, spent approximately $1,000 on materials, and built the baffles themselves—and they worked.

One afternoon, a team of engineers running a Morpheus test sparked a large grass fire on the grounds of JSC. The rocket heated its concrete pad, and a piece broke loose and was blown onto the grass field. It took almost four hours to get the fire under control after it seared a wide area of grass and burned more than 20 bales of hay intended for the longhorns that graze nearby. I could see the fire burning from my office in Building 20.

* * *

Altemus left NASA in 2013 and became one of three founders of a company called Intuitive Machines. Today, he serves as the president and CEO of the Houston company. The lander they developed, named Odysseus, became the first commercial lunar lander to complete a soft landing on the lunar surface. It was also the first U.S. spacecraft to land on the Moon in over fifty years.

The lander unexpectedly tipped to a 30-degree angle due to a last-minute technical issue, but all instruments onboard remained functional.

* * *

One of the activities I enjoyed during this period was taste-testing the food prepared by the Space Food Systems Lab that the astronauts would consume in space. The Food Lab would send an email announcing a taste-testing opportunity twice a month, and if I wasn't busy, I would reserve a time slot on their calendar. The Sensory Evaluation Center where the tests were conducted was a short walk from my office and only required about 15 minutes per test, so I volunteered as often as possible.

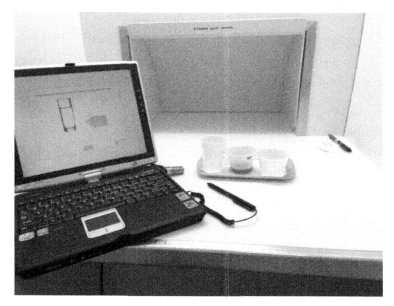

Setup in the JSC Food Lab for taste testing and rating astronaut food samples

In addition to other NASA employees, the astronauts themselves also participated in the taste tests, of course. I'm assuming their evaluations carried more weight than mine.

When you entered the testing center, you sat in a small cubicle—no talking with other testers was allowed—with a laptop to enter your ratings of the food you were testing. Once you were seated and signed in on the laptop, a sliding door opened and you were given a tray with a small sample of the food to be tested that day, along with three crackers and a small cup of water. The crackers and water allowed you to cleanse your palate before each bite.

After tasting the food, you were asked to rate the sample in five categories: appearance, color, aroma, flavor, and texture on a rating scale with nine levels ranging from "Dislike Extremely" to "Like Extremely." An additional yes/no question was "Did the food taste as you would expect it to taste?"

Some examples of the many different foods I taste-tested were grilled pork chop, broccoli and cheese casserole, BBQ nut bar, potatoes au gratin, curry sauce with vegetables, baked beans, ginger vanilla bar, and guacamole.

Given the restrictions on food preparation that the Food Lab has to deal with for space food, such as limiting sodium intake, I was pleasantly surprised by how much I liked almost every food I tried, with one exception—the guacamole.

I love guacamole, but the first time I taste-tested it at the evaluation center, I did not like the taste. I rated it poorly and wondered what the other testers thought, but since we were not allowed to chat with others about the test, I thought that perhaps it was just me.

A few weeks later, guacamole was on the menu again. Since I had not seen the same food tested more than once before, I presumed that I was not the only one unhappy with that first attempt. To my surprise and disappointment, the second attempt was also flavorless.

A few weeks after that, they offered a third tasting of guacamole. I thought, "They are determined to get this right!"— and they did on the third try. It was not the best guacamole I had ever tasted but, given the first two attempts, I was pleasantly surprised and could finally answer, yes—it tasted like I expected it to taste.

Several months later, I ran into Vickie Kloeris, Manager of the Space Food Systems Lab, and asked her about the guacamole. She said it had been specifically requested by a couple of astronauts but, in the end, they did not add it to the ISS menu because the short shelf life was too much of a problem—the same problem we have with guacamole here on Earth.

In space, foods are eaten out of pouches and plastic packages. Instead of a carving knife, scissors are more essential for meal preparation in space. On Earth, we can experience the aromas of food cooking and see the food on a plate.

Additionally, factors such as fluid shifts in the body, causing a stuffy nose from being weightless, and competing aromas can influence how food tastes. Most foods become bland and lack flavor in space because the sense of smell, a huge factor in how food tastes, is not as strong in space.

I've talked with several astronauts about their favorite food while in space. From what I've heard, shrimp cocktail is the most popular. It's a favorite because of the spicy, horseradish-based cocktail sauce that covers the shrimp.

* * *

Imagine being stuck in your house for months, unable to go to the grocery store or a restaurant whenever you have a food craving. You can only eat what is stored in your pantry, and those items were selected months earlier. Also, if your taste buds change, you are out of luck.

While on the ISS, Peggy Whitson once (jokingly) told an arriving Shuttle crew, which had just docked with the Station, that she wouldn't allow them on board until they confirmed that they had brought a resupply of hot sauce and salsa that she had requested.

While there is still no microwave oven on the ISS due to potential electromagnetic interference with other equipment onboard, food storage and preparation technology in space has been advancing recently. There was no refrigerator on the ISS until a couple of years ago. An ingenious refrigeration system called the Freezer Refrigerator Incubator Device for Galley and Experimentation, also known as the FRIDGE (Did I mention that NASA loves acronyms?) was added to the ISS. This should reduce the reliance on rehydrated foods.

NASA has successfully tested a small experimental Zero G oven, developed by Zero-G Kitchen, to bake cookies on the ISS—one cookie at a time. The cookies were baked at different temperatures for different periods of time. Unfortunately, the astronauts weren't allowed to eat the cookies they baked because those had to be returned to Earth for testing.

* * *

In December 2011, the Director of Procurement created a new office and redistributed the workload among the JSC Procurement Offices. The new office was named the Operations Support Office and would support the Mission Operations Directorate (MOD), the Flight Crew Operations Directorate (FCOD), the Center Director's Office (which included the Human Resources Office), the Safety and Mission Assurance (S&MA) Office, and the Chief Financial Officer's (CFO) Office.

24 - Flight Operations Support

I became manager of the new Operations Support Office on January 1, 2012, six months after the final Shuttle mission, STS-135. I was excited about the assignment because it meant that I could continue working with the Mission Operations and Flight Crew Operations groups that I had been supporting. I was also looking forward to working with the Safety & Mission Assurance office, led by former astronaut Bill McArthur.

* * *

Herb with his new office in the Apollo Mission Operations Control Room

JSC office managers like to occasionally take their offices to one of the many cool places on-site for group photos. Since my Operations Support Office was newly created, I arranged for our office photo to be taken in the Apollo Mission Control Room. For some, it was the first time they had visited that historic place. For most of the next three years, my deputy was Kristi Fryer, who was a pleasure to work with. Kristi had been a team lead in my previous office.

* * *

Former astronaut Mike Coats, who had flown on three Shuttle flights, was in his seventh year as the JSC director. He made his first spaceflight as the pilot on STS-41-D, the first flight for *Discovery*. The commander was Hank Hartsfield. The crew deployed three satellites from the payload bay.

Coats tells the story that when they first opened the payload bay, a Coke can floated up into view. It's not unusual for objects to float up when you are in zero gravity, especially during the first flight of a new Orbiter. When the Coke can floated up, he asked Hartsfield, "Think we ought to tell the ground about that?" Hartsfield said, "What are they going to do about it? Nothing." So, they never told Mission Control about the Coke can.

Coats also tells a Judy Resnik story regarding that flight. It was Judy's first flight. She had a full head of hair and when floating in zero gravity, it made for some memorable pictures. At one point, her hair accidentally got snagged in the IMAX camera they were using on that mission. Hartsfield was filming the deployment of a satellite from the payload bay when the IMAX camera's belt-driven magazine sucked in a portion of Resnik's floating hair.

The camera blew a circuit breaker and stopped working. They were able to free Resnik's hair with scissors and Coats began work on repairing the camera. Resnik glared at Hartsfield when he started to report the problem to ground controllers, so he simply told them that the camera had jammed and that they were working on it.

Coats worked for hours removing bits of Resnik's hair from the camera. He got it working again, and the commercially-funded footage they were shooting was completed. Someone must have secretly told mission controllers though, because the wake-up song the next morning was "Hair" from the Broadway musical.

* * *

I enjoyed Coats's tenure as director. He genuinely cared about all employees at JSC and was a believer in diversity and inclusion. One of the questions he asked when he took over was, "Are we a representative workforce? I want the best team here I can possibly get. I need the best players from every segment of our society. I want the best minorities. I want the best females. I want the best gays and lesbians. I want the best from every group. I want them to feel like they're welcome, and they fit in immediately here at JSC." Another initiative  started while Coats was director was Employee Resource Groups, or ERGs. Employee Resource Groups are voluntary, employee-led groups with the goal of promoting a diverse, inclusive workplace. The groups are led by employees and include members that share a characteristic such as lifestyle, ethnicity, gender, or religion, as well as their allies. The ERG program has been very successful and continues today. There are now at least 11 different ERGs at JSC.

* * *

NASA Administrator Charlie Bolden made the final decision on where the three remaining Shuttle Orbiter vehicles would go after the Shuttle Program ended. NASA formed a recommendation team that developed five options for placing the Orbiters, which it presented to Bolden.

Bolden's emphasis was on reaching the largest number of visitors. After soliciting another round of interested museums in January 2010, the team ranked the 13 eligible institutions according to nine criteria.

In April 2011, NASA announced that *Atlantis* would go to the KSC Visitor Complex, *Endeavour* would go to the California Science Center, *Discovery* would go to the Steven F. Udvar-Hazy Center in northern Virginia, and *Enterprise*, which had been at the Udvar-Hazy since 2003, would be moved to the Intrepid Sea, Air & Space Museum in New York City.

The decision not to award an Orbiter to Houston was a shock to many at JSC and in the Houston area. How could Space City—home of the astronauts—not be awarded one of the Orbiters to display? There are still hard feelings about that decision among many here in Houston.

The good news is that Space Center Houston was awarded the Shuttle Carrier Aircraft which transported the Orbiters around the country. In addition, a high-fidelity, full-size Orbiter mockup, called *Explorer*, which had been on display at the Kennedy Space Center since 1994, was moved to Space Center Houston in 2012. *Explorer* is the highest fidelity mockup of the Orbiter ever built. It was built by a company in Florida using schematics, blueprints, and archival documents loaned by NASA and its Shuttle contractors.

The mockup was renamed *Independence* once it was moved to Space Center Houston. After the Shuttle Carrier Aircraft arrived at Space Center Houston, there was a ceremony in August 2014 where the public could watch *Independence* being lifted with cranes and placed atop the SCA. I attended the event that morning, where astronaut Eileen Collins spoke.

Space Center Houston is today the most popular tourist attraction in Houston and was recently named the "Best Museum in Texas" by USA Today. It draws 1.2 million visitors every year, with 33% coming from other countries. I would have been happy if Space Center Houston had been awarded a flown Orbiter vehicle, but I believe the combination of an Orbiter vehicle mockup that you can walk inside, sitting atop a Shuttle Carrier Aircraft, that you can also walk inside, is not a bad consolation prize. The flown Orbiter vehicles are permanently sealed and cannot be touched by visitors.

* * *

Herb with Space Shuttle Endeavour at Ellington Field

In September 2012, Space Shuttle *Endeavour* made a stopover in Houston at Ellington Field on her way to the California Science Center in Los Angeles. Before landing at Ellington, the SCA with *Endeavour* atop flew several low-altitude circles above JSC so that all employees could walk outside their office to watch it fly over. I received a VIP pass to see *Endeavour* atop the SCA up close the following day.

Once *Endeavour* arrived at Los Angeles International Airport (LAX) and was de-mated from the SCA, it was placed on the same large transporter device that NASA had used to move Orbiters between Palmdale and Edwards AFB. The trip from LAX to the Science Center through the streets of Los Angeles took two days, moving at about 1-2 mph. There were huge crowds viewing the trip, all along the route, which had been published in advance.

To avoid trees and other obstacles along the route, the Shuttle zigzagged between them. *Endeavour* arrived at the Science Center 15 hours later than planned, but without hitting a single object along the way.

Since its arrival at the Science Center, *Endeavour* has been displayed horizontally. However, the Science Center plans to display *Endeavour* vertically, with solid rocket boosters and an external tank attached. The process of displaying *Endeavour* in the vertical launch position began in July 2023. Stacking the Shuttle system in this vertical position has never been done outside the VAB at KSC.

* * *

In December 2012, Mike Coats retired from NASA after seven years as center director and Ellen Ochoa, who had been the Deputy Director, took over as director in January 2013. Ellen was the eighth different JSC Director that I worked under: Dr. Chris Kraft, Gerry Griffin, Jesse Moore, George Abbey, Roy Estess (Acting), Jefferson Howell, Mike Coats, and Ellen. One of the first actions Ellen took was naming Steve Altemus, the Director of Engineering, as her Deputy Director. Lauri Hansen, who I had worked with when she was leading the *Altair* lunar lander project under the Constellation Program, took Steve's place as Director of Engineering.

Ellen was the first Hispanic woman in space and the second woman to be JSC Director (after Carolyn Huntoon, who was director during the years that I was at NASA Headquarters). Ellen was selected as an astronaut in January 1991 and flew on four Shuttle missions but is most proud of the fact that there have been six schools named after her.

I heard Ellen talk about how difficult it was for her and other women wanting to be engineers or scientists to be taken seriously when she was going to college in the 1970s. She talked about enrolling at San Diego State and trying to explore subjects that involved math. She went to see two professors— one in the electrical engineering department and one in the physics department. The engineering professor made it clear that she didn't fit his picture of what an engineer looked like. He told her, "Well, we had a woman come through the program once, but it's a difficult subject and one that you might not be interested in."

She got a much different reception from the physics professor. He was glad to hear she was interested in the subject and told her about some of the careers she could have if she majored in physics. When he heard she was completing calculus, he told her, "That's great! You've already learned the language of physics. When you start the semester, you'll be able to concentrate on the concepts while many of the students will be trying to learn that and the math part simultaneously." Ellen would eventually earn a bachelor of science degree in physics with a minor in math from San Diego State.

Ellen wanted to do research, so she went to Stanford for graduate school and started in 1981, the year of the first Shuttle flight, which she described as a "wonderful new vehicle where you could do research in space." Sally Ride would become the first American woman in space two years later. Sally had also studied physics and had gone to school at Stanford. Ellen says she needed to see all those connections for her to conceive of the fact that joining the astronaut corps was something she could do.

* * *

In 2013, Italian astronaut Luca Parmitano almost drowned during an ISS spacewalk when a significant amount of water leaked into his helmet. About 45 minutes into the EVA, Parmitano radioed Mission Control to let them know that he was feeling a lot of water on the back of his head. This is unusual when you consider the way water acts in zero-gravity. In space, water doesn't run down the back of your neck and soak your clothes. It sticks to your skin like a gel.

The volume of water in his helmet continued to grow over the next few minutes. Chris Cassidy, his spacewalk partner, stopped working and joined Parmitano, trying to help determine what the problem was. Cassidy was thinking it must be coming from his water bag, but Parmitano didn't think so. The astronauts have a drink bag full of water in the front of their spacesuit, with a straw that allows them to drink.

Parmitano drank all of the water in his bag to see if that would stop it from entering his helmet, but that didn't work. His head was very wet and he felt like the water was getting into his ears. He began to think that the water flowing through the

Liquid Cooling & Ventilation Garment (LCVG) he was wearing was the source of the water in his helmet, but that possibility was ruled out by flight controllers.

After the water volume continued to increase with no idea of where it was coming from, the EVA was terminated and the astronauts were instructed to return to the airlock. Unfortunately, Parmitano and Cassidy were on opposite sides of the ISS at the time, so Parmitano had to return on his own.

Making things worse, the sun had just gone behind the Earth as Parmitano headed back inside so it was now dark, he couldn't see, couldn't communicate, and he was alone. He couldn't even see the hand holds he was supposed to use to make his way to the airlock. He had to rely on memory and feel his way back to find it. He didn't know how much time he had before the water covered his mouth and drowned him.

He managed to find the airlock where Cassidy joined him. After both were inside, the airlock was repressurized. The inner lock was opened, and crew member Karen Nyberg removed Parmitano's helmet, releasing a burst of water droplets. He estimated that they wiped about 1/3 gallon of water from his head and helmet.

EVA 22, one week earlier, had been completed by the same two astronauts wearing the same spacesuits without any apparent problems. However, after the spacewalk was over, Parmitano's communications cap was completely soaked. He assumed the water had come from his drink bag, so no investigation of the problem was conducted. For EVA 23, the drink bag was simply swapped for another as the solution.

After an investigation into the EVA 23 incident, it was determined that the mishap was caused by small bits of aluminum silicate plugging holes in the water separator. Water filters failed, allowing particulates to enter the suit's water filtration system. In the zero-gravity environment, this allowed water to flow around the fan blade and into Luca's helmet.

Looking back on it, the EVA should have been terminated (or aborted) when Parmitano first mentioned that he had water in his helmet. Small amounts of water had collected in helmets on previous EVAs, but no spacewalker had ever experienced that much water in their helmet that early in a spacewalk.

Herb with Luca Parmitano at the Johnson Space Center

Parmitano and I both worked at the Johnson Space Center during this time period. I was able to talk with him a couple of times and asked him about that spacewalk. He told me that his heart rate, which was being monitored on the ground in Houston, didn't increase as he was trying to find his way back to the airlock to get back inside the ISS. That amazed me, but I shouldn't have been so surprised. He is a former test pilot for the Italian Air Force, is a triathlete, and has had extensive training in dealing with very stressful, dangerous situations. His calmness here probably saved his life.

* * *

In November 2013, Canadian astronaut Chris Hadfield, who had written a book called *An Astronaut's Guide to Life on Earth*, had a combination lunch and book signing event in Houston that I attended. It was a small group of about 25 to 30 people having lunch. Apollo astronauts Alan Bean and Walt Cunningham, who both lived in Houston, were also there seated at the table next to mine.

Hadfield spoke to the group while we were eating lunch, telling us how he is afraid of heights and how, when he is standing near the edge of a cliff or looking over the railing of a balcony in a high-rise, his stomach starts tumbling, his palms sweat, and his legs don't want to move even though the rising panic in his body is insisting that he get back to safety. Yet he had performed two spacewalks on his second spaceflight, STS-100. He said that many hours of training for spacewalks in the Neutral Buoyancy Lab made it possible for him to feel relatively comfortable stepping outside a spacecraft traveling at 17,500 miles per hour. After lunch, not only did Hadfield autograph my copy of his book, Alan Bean also signed the book for me.

* * *

One of the organizational decisions Ellen Ochoa made as director was to combine the Mission Operations Directorate (MOD) and the Flight Crew Operations Directorate (FCOD) —both of which my office was supporting—into one operations group called the Flight Operations Directorate (FOD) in August 2014. The two organizations had been together at one point in NASA's history but they had been split into two different groups sometime in the 1980s.

Ellen wanted to make it an integrated organization. For example, there had been engineers who supported the

Astronaut Office (under FCOD) and there were also engineers that supported the Flight Director's Office (under MOD). The two groups were essentially trying to do the same thing, but they didn't talk to each other. Ellen said that her goal was to change the mindset from "We support mission control" or "We support the astronauts" to "We're working together to have a successful mission."

The change reduced the number of direct reports to the director, provided a better collaboration environment for crew and operations training, and allowed a wider variety of career paths for people in those directorates. There were other mergers of organizations and directorates around the center to streamline the management chain reporting to Ellen, but this was the most significant one.

Naturally, there was a lot of speculation about who would be selected as the director of the new FOD. Most people assumed that either the incumbent Director of MOD, Paul Hill, or the incumbent Director of FCOD, Janet Kavandi, would get that job. After having worked closely with Brian "BK" Kelly, who was the Deputy Director of FCOD, I suspected that he might be the choice. It was not a huge surprise to me when Ellen announced that BK would head the new FOD organization. Within a few months, Paul Hill had left NASA, and Janet Kavandi had moved to the Glenn Research Center as their deputy center director.

The joke among the former MOD folks was, "I am now a piece of FOD," which is also an acronym for Foreign Object Debris or Foreign Object Damage—not what you want to be in the world of flying.

After the new Flight Operations Directorate was formed, BK invited me to attend his staff meeting every Monday morning at 7:30 a.m. In addition to BK, the meeting attendees included the Deputy Director of FOD, the Chief and Deputy Chief of the Astronaut Office, the Chief of Spaceflight Training, the Chief Flight Director, the Chief of the Aircraft Operations Division, and both the NASA managers and the contractor managers of the Neutral Buoyancy Lab and the Space Vehicle Mockup Facility, among others.

Since the Mission Control operations ran 24/7, it wasn't unusual for the Chief Flight Director to tell a story at those Monday morning meetings about something unusual that happened over the weekend while most of us were off-duty. There was also a presentation on the status of each individual astronaut on the ISS, showing how many hours they had worked the previous week. That was tracked closely because NASA wanted to make certain that the astronauts had sufficient time off and were not being overworked.

One Monday morning in October 2016, I pulled into the parking lot near Building 1 shortly after 7:00 a.m. on my way to the FOD staff meeting. The FOD offices and conference room were on the 8th floor of Building 1, one floor below the center director's suite of offices. As I stepped out of my car, a van parked nearby and a large group stepped out. They seemed to be unusually energetic for that time of the morning. They were all smiling, laughing and patting each other on the back as I followed them toward the doors of Building 1.

I thought to myself, "How can they be in such a good mood this early on a Monday morning?" Once the staff meeting started, I learned that they were the first group of 12 potential astronaut candidates (AsCans) arriving for their interviews with the astronaut selection panel that day. Suddenly, their frivolity made sense. NASA would eventually select seven men and five women for Astronaut Group 22, announced in June 2017.

* * *

One of the many Employee Resource Groups at JSC is the Women Excelling in Life and Leadership (WELL) group. In April 2015, the WELL ERG held a panel discussion, which I attended, featuring five women astronauts who spoke about work/life balance, challenges they had faced, and other stories and unique experiences. The astronauts were Karen Nyberg, Anna Fisher, Nicole Stott, Stephanie Wilson, and Serena Auñón-Chancellor. It was a unique opportunity to hear personal stories from this accomplished group of women.

Panel of women astronauts at JSC – L to R: Karen Nyberg, Anna Fisher, Nicole Stott, Stephanie Wilson, & Serena Auñón-Chancellor

* * *

In the summer of 2014, after working with the MOD/FOD folks for several years and getting to better know the people and the facilities they managed, such as the Neutral Buoyancy Lab, Space Vehicle Mockup Facility, and Mission Control Centers, I inquired about gaining access to those areas for myself.

Access is generally restricted to NASA employees who work in those areas daily, so approval is required to have your badge coded for acceptance by the card reader at the entrances.

With the help of Joy Barckholtz, who was on the FOD staff but was on loan to the Procurement Office for a special assignment, my request for access was approved, including a Deck Pass for the NBL, which allowed access to the pool deck.

Over the next few years, I estimate that I gave 40 to 50 tours to groups and individuals, including 10 tours during my last week prior to retirement—enjoying every one of them. During one of the tours, an NBL worker thanked me for guiding the group through the facility, because it meant that he didn't have to take time away from his job to guide those tours. (It's a tough job, but someone has to do it...)

* * *

That Neutral Buoyancy Lab, where astronauts can simulate weightlessness in the pool to train for spacewalks, was a favorite facility to visit. It is the largest indoor pool in the U.S. and currently has mockups of most of the ISS modules sunk at the bottom of the pool. The mockups are made mostly of stainless steel, titanium, plastics, and some aluminum, and are built next door to the NBL in the Light Manufacturing Facility.

When an object is made neutrally buoyant (through either adding weight or flotation devices), it neither floats nor sinks. In that situation, even a heavy object can be easily manipulated, much as it is in the zero gravity of space, but there are two major differences between the neutral buoyancy achieved in the NBL and weightlessness in space.

The first is that astronauts in spacesuits training in the NBL are not actually weightless. While they are neutrally buoyant, they feel their weight while in their spacesuits. The second is that the drag of the water hampers their motion, making some tasks easier and others more difficult than in zero gravity. Despite these differences, neutral buoyancy is the best method available for astronauts to train for spacewalks.

Prior to building the pool at its current location, there were plans to build the new facility on JSC property. It was intended to be even larger—235 feet long by 135 feet wide—than the current NBL. However, within weeks of groundbreaking on the JSC property, it was decided to move the pool to its current location. To save money and fit inside its building, the size of the pool was reduced to its current dimensions: 202 feet long by 102 feet wide by 40 feet deep.

The building that houses the NBL was originally built by McDonnell Douglas to be a Space Station Processing Facility for Space Station Freedom under Work Package 2. Once Russia and the other partners were brought into the program and it became the ISS, the contract to process ISS elements was awarded to Boeing, which built the Space Station Processing Facility in Florida on KSC property.

This left the building in Houston vacant and available. Construction of the NBL began in 1994 with the removal of the slab and 23,000 cubic yards of dirt. This created a hole in the building floor that was 27 feet deep. Next, a water pumping system was installed to remove groundwater from around the foundation of the pool floor. The pool floor was then framed and 528 truckloads (5,300 cubic yards) of concrete were brought in for a continuous pour of the floor. The pool floor is made of concrete that is six feet thick. The walls were then poured, requiring another 3,500 cubic yards of concrete (350 truckloads).

The NBL holds 6.2 million gallons of water, weighing approximately 50 million pounds. After it was built, it took a month to fill the entire pool—a volume equivalent to that of 560 backyard swimming pools. Since the filters are near the top, the water turned green from algae by the time it was filled. Once the filters and chemical systems were turned on, it took another month for the pool to be clear. The pool is chlorinated, just like a backyard swimming pool.

With the Deck Pass, I could take visitors onto the floor of the NBL around the pool, but a fair amount of coordination and scheduling in advance with the NBL Operations Center was required to get approval for those visits. It was more difficult to schedule tours of the NBL than tours of the SVMF and the Mission Control rooms.

* * *

One of the first opportunities I had to use my new badge coded for access to the restricted areas came that summer when a friend, Maia Weinstock, the deputy editor of MIT News, contacted me about a possible visit to JSC. My older son and his wife are MIT alumni, and I had met Maia on one of my trips to the campus in Cambridge, MA.

Maia is an advocate for girls and women, writing often about the history of women in STEM and diversity in STEM media. We initially met because she was interested in the work Mom had done on the parasol for the Skylab Program.

In 2014, Maia traveled to Austin, TX, to guest-curate a display called "Portraits of Women in Science" at the Art Science Gallery, featuring more than 30 prominent women in the STEM fields. She asked if I would give her a tour of JSC if she made a stop in Houston on her way home.

She also wanted to know if I could arrange for her to meet with Ellen Ochoa while there. Once I got on Ellen's calendar, Maia was considered a Center Director's Guest, and a public affairs specialist was assigned to conduct the tour. I simply tagged along.

Maia Weinstock presenting LEGO gift to Ellen Ochoa

Maia, known internationally for her custom LEGO designs, presented Ellen with a framed, custom-made minifigure of Ellen holding a flute during our meeting.

It was two years after this visit to JSC that Maia created the *Women of NASA* LEGO set. The official LEGO set was released in 2017 and became a bestseller.

* * *

In April 2015, Andy Weir, author of the best-selling book *The Martian*, visited JSC and spoke to employees, answered questions, and signed copies of his book. After reading his book and being impressed with how much he seemed to know about NASA and astronauts, I was surprised when he revealed, "Before I arrived here (at JSC) yesterday, I had never met an astronaut in person."

Weir has a fear of flying, so in 2013, when he found himself signing large contracts for the publishing and film rights to his novel, he conducted all transactions over the phone. Since he had never met the people he was talking to in Los Angeles and New York, he worried that all of this attention was a hoax.

He had almost given up hope of becoming a published author after having no luck finding any publisher interested in his work. Luckily for him, the posting of his book online created so much interest that a publishing company and movie studio were offering him six-figure deals. The publishing deal and the movie deal were done four days apart while he was still doing his day job as a computer programmer, fixing software bugs.

He was so shocked by this sudden reversal of fortune that he was afraid that it must be a scam. After he started receiving the checks, he thought to himself, "If it's a scam, then they're not very good at it."

NASA assisted the filmmakers with portraying the science and technology in *The Martian* because of its potential to promote interest in space exploration. Over the next month, NASA answered hundreds of questions and sent numerous files of actual photos of Mars and control centers, including images of the control center's computer screens, to the film's production team.

A few months after Weir's visit, Mackenzie Davis and Sebastian Stan, two of the co-stars in *The Martian* movie, visited JSC for a discussion with Ellen Ochoa and astronaut Mike Hopkins in JSC's Teague auditorium. The following evening, I attended a private screening for NASA employees of *The Martian* movie, two weeks before its official release in the U.S. I enjoyed the movie so much that I returned to see it a second time.

* * *

In June, astronaut Shane Kimbrough, who lived near my friend Robbie LaBrier, offered to give Robbie and a small group of his friends a personally guided tour of the ISS mockup in the Space Vehicle Mockup Facility, as a birthday present. Robbie kindly included me in the group. Kimbrough spent an hour showing us around the ISS mockup and answering questions.

Kimbrough had flown on STS-126 as a Mission Specialist and was in training for his next assignment, launching to the ISS on Soyuz MS-02 as a member of Expedition 49/50, with Peggy Whitson and others. Shane would serve as ISS Commander for Expedition 50. Two years later, during that mission, I had the opportunity to talk with both Kimbrough and Whitson on a live video downlink with the ISS in the IMAX theater at Space Center Houston.

* * *

The Mission Operations and Flight Crew Operations (now combined into Flight Operations) offices have held an annual party in the fall called Fajita Festival for many years. The first one I attended occurred in October 2015. It's held in a large hangar at Ellington Field. Unsurprisingly, the meal consists of fajitas with all the trimmings and a margarita machine working overtime. There's a live band for entertainment and the astronauts are serving the meals and working the margarita machine. I'm guessing there were 250 people in attendance that evening, including astronauts, flight directors, astronaut trainers, pilots, and flight controllers.

I'm not sure if it was great planning or coincidence, but the ISS passed over Houston during the event that night. Most of the partygoers stepped outside the hangar to watch the flyover at the precise time it passed overhead. I was standing next to astronaut Mike Fossum, and as we both watched the ISS fly across the sky, I said to him, "You spent 6 months up there a few years ago, didn't you?" He replied, "Yes, and I would go back in a heartbeat."

* * *

Several months later, I met a few of my co-workers for a happy hour at Chelsea Wine Bar, a few miles from JSC. Shortly after arriving, I saw astronaut Cady Coleman walk in and go upstairs. After our group broke up for the evening, I went upstairs to see who else might be there.

I was pleasantly surprised to see Cady playing her flute with the astronaut band, Bandella. In addition to Cady, Chris Hadfield was playing rhythm guitar, astronaut Dan Burbank was playing guitar, astronaut Steve Robinson was playing a stand-up bass guitar, and Micki Pettit, wife of astronaut Don Pettit, was singing vocals. Naturally, I stayed until they finished their set. What a nice surprise that was.

Bandella performing upstairs at Chelsea Wine Bar near JSC

Occasionally, when one of the Bandella members was in orbit, the rest of the band would gather on Earth and they would play together with the astronaut in space. I've heard Cady

Coleman tell a story about how she once had a routine medical conference with the doctors on the ground and, when she finished, the rest of the band was waiting for her. She had taken her flute to the Cupola, and they played together for about 30 minutes and were almost done when the ISS Master Alarm went off. At that point, all of the astronauts drop whatever they're doing and go to the central post. They determine what has happened, talk to the ground, and decide what, if anything, they have to do. In this case, it turned out to be nothing to worry about and they all went on with their work.

At the end of the day, Cady was going to play her flute but couldn't find it. She had no recollection of playing it earlier in the Cupola. On the ISS, there's a lot of airflow, and that's where they find most of their lost items—clinging to the vents. That's where Cady found her flute.

* * *

In February 2016, I was called into an FOD meeting with BK Kelly, Bob Behnken (Chief of the Astronaut Office), Greg "Ray-J" Johnson (Chief of Aircraft Operations), and several other FOD staff members. At the time, all NASA astronauts traveled to the ISS on the Russian Soyuz spacecraft, launched from the Baikonur Cosmodrome in Kazakhstan.

They also returned from the ISS on their Soyuz spacecraft which landed in Kazakhstan. NASA has a Gulfstream III (G-III) jet aircraft that was used to fly astronauts to Baikonur for launch and was also used to pick up the astronauts from the Krayniy Airport in Baikonur after they returned to Earth.

The meeting was to develop a contingency plan for picking up astronaut Scott Kelly in Kazakhstan after his year-long ISS mission ended in March 2016, as the G-III aircraft needed repairs. The parts needed to make the repair had been ordered but there was concern that the parts would not arrive in time to complete the repair and pick up Kelly.

I was asked to make plans to charter an aircraft to be flown to Kazakhstan at the last minute if the parts did not arrive in time to repair the G-III. One of the many things I loved about working for NASA was that it was never boring. Every day was interesting and challenging, and you never knew when you might be asked to do something you had never done before. I had never chartered an aircraft before but it was an interesting exercise (especially since I did not have to worry about paying for it with my own money).

Thankfully, the parts for the G-III aircraft arrived in time to make the repair and pick up Kelly after his Expedition 45/46 mission ended. However, that potential problem with the G-III was the impetus for BK deciding that NASA needed a newer, faster, more reliable, longer-range aircraft for transporting our astronauts to and from Kazakhstan. The G-III aircraft was at least 30 years old and had to make multiple stops on flights between Houston and Kazakhstan.

Shortly after Scott Kelly returned home, BK tasked me with acquiring a Gulfstream V (G-V). The G-Vs were only 15-20 years old, larger, faster, capable of flying higher, and had twice the range of a G-III (5,000 miles compared to 2,400 miles). Hourly operating costs for a G-V are also approximately 20-25 percent lower than the G-III due to increased fuel efficiency and less costly long-term engine maintenance.

The Gulfstream V could also make the trip between Houston and Kazakhstan non-stop, but to do so would require flying over the North Pole. NASA did not want to fly that path, so they instead planned to make one stop in either Europe (e.g., Scotland) or the Eastern U.S. (e.g., Maine), depending on real-time weather conditions, for refueling.

261

Due to strict Federal regulations on the use and acquisition of government aircraft, the first hurdle in this project was to obtain approval from NASA Headquarters to acquire the G-V aircraft. In May 2016, JSC Director Ellen Ochoa signed a letter requesting approval from the Assistant Administrator for Strategic Infrastructure for JSC's acquisition of a "Long-Range Aircraft."

Once that approval was received, my office developed a procurement plan and a schedule for conducting the competitive acquisition and FOD asked that I be appointed as the Source Selection Official, which meant that I would select which plane to buy from those offered in the competition. The initial schedule had a completion date of February 2017, allowing us approximately eight months to solicit bids, evaluate them, make the selection, and award the contract.

That schedule seemed fine at first but, early that summer, BK asked that we complete the acquisition by September 30, the last day of the Government fiscal year, rather than in February 2017. His concern was that 2016 was an election year and there would be a new president in January. He did not want to risk either having our acquisition zeroed out in the new FY 2017 budget or having a new administration cancel it upon taking office.

I had serious doubts that we could pull off this acquisition in four months instead of the nine months we had initially planned for, but we were going to give it our best shot, hope that we had no major obstacles would arise during the process, and wish for some luck along the way.

As August approached, we were making good progress with few problems encountered, but time was running out. One story I can laugh about now, though it wasn't funny at the time, is what occurred during those Monday morning FOD staff meetings in late August and early September. BK would go around the room, asking everyone if they had anything to report. When he got to me, before I could speak, he would point his finger and simply say, "September 30th," before moving to the next person.

Herb with the Gulfstream V aircraft that his office acquired for JSC

In late August, we received proposals from four brokers for five different aircraft. In mid-September, after evaluating the proposed aircraft and performing inspections, I selected a G-V that had been a corporate jet for Nike, based in Oregon, at a price of $13 million.

Though I was responsible for selecting the aircraft, I worked closely with astronaut Greg 'Ray-J' Johnson throughout the process, as he was the Chief of Aircraft Operations at JSC.

To my great relief, we executed the contract with no problems, and the plane arrived from Oregon at Ellington Field on September 29—one day early! Those of us involved in the acquisition celebrated with a ceremony at Ellington Field, attended by BK and Ellen Ochoa, the following day—Friday,

September 30. I'm amazed at how fortunate we were that so many steps along the way happened exactly as we needed them to for us to meet that deadline. Eight years later, the plane is still performing well for JSC.

* * *

In April 2016, a friend who lives in Wisconsin asked me if I would take her and her two daughters on a tour of JSC. Her birthday was approaching and she wanted to do something special with her daughters to celebrate—a trip to NASA and the beach (Galveston). I told her that I would be happy to be their tour guide.

Herb with visitors and astronaut Luca Parmitano at JSC's Rocket Park

The day they arrived in Houston, I took them to see the popular sights at JSC (Apollo Mission Control, the Mockup Facility, and the NBL), and we ended the day at Rocket Park, where a Saturn V rocket is on display. When we entered the building that late afternoon, it was empty except for a small group at the base of the rocket. The group was a woman with a cameraman interviewing Italian astronaut Luca Parmitano.

As we walked by, they were speaking Italian, so we couldn't understand what they were saying. We continued walking around the rocket and were near the Command Module at the rocket's opposite end when one of the daughters asked, "Is it OK if we go back and see if they're finished with the interview, so we can maybe meet the astronaut?" "No problem," I said.

The interview with Luca was ending as we approached the group. I introduced my friends to Luca, and he graciously spent 10 to 15 minutes chatting and taking photos with us. It was the perfect ending to our day.

* * *

Scott Kelly with Herb's guests prior to a JSC tour

Speaking of running into astronauts while giving tours of JSC, that happened several other times as well. Since my visitors had to enter JSC in my car—vehicles aren't allowed to enter JSC unless the driver has a NASA ID—I would often meet my visitors at a coffee shop across the street. On one occasion, I was there to pick up a group of friends for a tour and we bumped into Scott Kelly, who had recently returned from his year-long mission on the ISS. Scott talked with us briefly and posed for photos with our group.

On another occasion, my tour group met Jessica Meir, who was conducting her own tour for a group in the Space Vehicle Mockup Facility. Several weeks later, I ran into Jessica again while touring a friend through the Apollo Mission Control Room where Jessica was taking photos with a new camera she was learning how to use. On both occasions, she took the time for photos with my guests.

Herb with Jessica Mier in the Space Vehicle Mockup Facility at JSC

Another day, I was showing family members around the Space Vehicle Mockup Facility and ran into Cady Coleman, who stopped to talk and take photos with us. But my favorite story about unexpectedly running into an astronaut while showing someone around JSC was with a new hire at JSC, Julie Read. I had taken Julie into Building 4S, where the astronauts' offices are, and as we stood near the elevators on the first floor, I mentioned that we might see an astronaut.

The elevator doors opened, and astronaut Tracy Caldwell Dyson stepped out. As I was turning to point her out, I heard Tracy say, "Julie!" and Julie said, "Tracy!" I looked at them both and said, "Wait a minute. You two know each other?" They had recently met at a conference.

* * *

Herb with Suni Williams at the Johnson Space Center

The day after Super Bowl 51 (when New England beat Atlanta 34-28 after trailing 28-3 in the 3rd quarter), I was leaving Building 1, headed to the cafeteria when I ran into Suni Williams, who was also headed to the cafeteria. We struck up a conversation about the game as we walked to lunch. Just a typical day at the Johnson Space Center.

* * *

In May, I was contacted by a journalist from Poland, Joanna Skrzypiec, who was a Fellow at the Center for Strategic & International Studies in Washington, D.C. She wanted to interview me for an article about space that she was writing for Poland's edition of *Business Insider*.

We met at the coffee shop when she arrived in Houston and she asked me about several topics, including *The Martian* movie, how cooperation with Russia was going, the commercial space industry, what the different NASA centers were responsible for, and the *Challenger* accident. Since she was not a U.S. citizen, I could not take her on-site at JSC, so I took her on a tour of Space Center Houston instead. The article she eventually published of my interview is still posted online, but it's in Polish.

* * *

It is well known how much NASA loves acronyms. NASA itself is an acronym. There is often an attempt to be creative with acronyms when naming contracts because those acronyms, rather than the actual contract numbers, are more easily used to identify contracts. At JSC, only a few contracts are widely recognized by their contract numbers.

I can think of only three of those over the past 50 years: the Space Shuttle contract awarded to Rockwell (NAS9-14000), the ISS contract awarded to Boeing (NAS15-10000), and the Space Flight Operations Contract awarded to United Space Alliance (NAS9-20000). As you can see, they were all given special numbers with lots of zeros.

Some organizations have gone so far as to create contract names and acronyms honoring individual people in the procurement office who support those contracts. When it was time to award a new contract for aircraft operations and maintenance, the name **A**ircraft Maintenance, **L**ogistics, **I**ntegration, **C**onfiguration Management, and **E**ngineering, which gives you the acronym ALICE, was created. This was done to honor Alice Pursell, who has worked for many years supporting aircraft operations and was the contracting officer for our G-V acquisition.

I recently learned that the follow-on to the ALICE contract was named **C**ompre**H**ensive **A**ircraft **R**eadiness, **L**ifecycle, **E**ngineering, and **S**upport, which gives you CHARLES as an acronym, to honor Charles Bell, who followed me as the manager of the Operations Support Office.

* * *

An interesting coincidence arose during the summer of 2016. A fellow trombone player from the University of Texas Longhorn Band and long-time friend, Bill Brent, had become a band director at McCallum High School in Austin after graduation from UT. Bill and I are still in touch and that spring, he mentioned that he had unexpectedly received a telephone call from space.

The call was from astronaut Tim Kopra, who was on the ISS at the time as part of Expedition 46/47. Bill had no involvement in the space program, so I was curious about this story. Bill explained that while he was the band director at McCallum High School, Tim Kopra had been the band's drum major in 1980-81, and they had developed a close relationship.

Shortly thereafter, I attended the welcome home ceremony for the Expedition 46/47 astronauts at JSC and had the opportunity to talk with Kopra. I said to him, "You and I have a mutual friend. Your high school band director, Bill Brent, is a friend and former college classmate of mine." Kopra's eyes lit up, and he replied, 'Yes! Bill has been a huge influence in my life. In addition to learning a lot from him about leadership while in the band, he also wrote a letter of recommendation that helped me get into West Point. I'll always be thankful for Bill's friendship." I admit I'm envious of Bill. I have never received a phone call from an astronaut on the ISS.

Herb with astronaut Tim Kopra at JSC after Kopra returned from his Expedition 46/47 mission

* * *

In early October, after completing the G-V acquisition, I was just three months away from my planned retirement date of January 3, 2017. Since my career would be winding down and the Thanksgiving and Christmas holiday seasons would soon be upon us, I assumed those final three months would be uneventful. I'm happy to say that it did not turn out as I had expected.

First, the JSC Director of Procurement made me a Special Assistant to the Director on her staff. The main reason for this move was to allow someone to take over my job as manager of the Operations Support Office while I was still working, ensuring a smooth transition. The most interesting thing about that transition was that they replaced me with three people. While I was manager of the office, I had one deputy manager and two team leads working for me. After I retired, they selected a new manager, added an additional deputy and an additional team lead, without changing the workload.

The best part of this new staff position was attending meetings with Ellen Ochoa and other JSC Senior Staff members in place of my boss when she was too busy to attend.

When astronauts return from an ISS mission, they have a debriefing of their flight with the center director and JSC Senior Staff shortly after returning, recapping their mission and answering questions.

Meeting with Ellen Ochoa and Jeff Williams during his mission debriefing to JSC Senior Staff

In October, I attended one of those debriefings session where Jeff Williams discussed his Expedition 47/48 mission. It was his fourth space flight and he had been the ISS Commander for Expedition 48. He also broke Scott Kelly's American record of 520 cumulative days in space on that mission by reaching 534 cumulative days before returning to Earth in September. [Note: Peggy Whitson broke that record a few months later with 675 days in space, but Williams still held the record for an American man.]

During the Q&A part of the debriefing, I asked Williams, "After four space flights, are you hoping to go back for a fifth time?" He grinned and replied, "I'll have to check with my wife before I can answer that. She probably thinks I've spent enough time up there."

* * *

During this same period, I was asked by Ellen Ochoa to be a co-chair of JSC's Combined Federal Campaign (CFC), an annual workplace charity campaign throughout the Federal government, typically occurring from October through December. My co-chair was Paul Gramm, a young astronautical engineer working in FOD.

That assignment kept Paul and me busy attending staff meetings across the center, making presentations to organizations, answering questions, and providing information and forms for those wanting to make donations. We attended Ellen's weekly Senior Staff meeting to provide an update on the progress we were making towards our goal.

An enjoyable part of this assignment was when Ellen asked us to set up a table in the JSC cafeteria one day during lunchtime, where she joined us for an hour. As we tried to convince employees entering the cafeteria to make a donation, Ellen and I had a long conversation about topics like playing musical instruments (she plays the flute), college football (she's a huge Stanford football fan), kids, acting, and living on the ISS (where she spent almost 21 days).

L to R Paul Gramm, Ellen Ochoa, Herb, & Kenesha Starling in the JSC Cafeteria soliciting donations for the Combined Federal Campaign (CFC)

By the end of December, we had met our JSC goal for employee contributions to the CFC. It was a pleasure working with Paul, who is currently a Flight Activities Officer (FAO) in Mission Control. I spotted him working at the FAO console when I watched the uncrewed Artemis I launch from the Mission Control viewing room in November 2022.

* * *

In November, we had a visitor from NASA Headquarters who was relatively new to NASA and had never visited JSC. I was asked to show her around the center, and she specifically requested to see the Lunar Sample Lab in Building 31N, so I arranged the tour. The lab provides a secure, contamination-free environment for the storage of the lunar sample collection.

The lunar samples are well-protected to keep them in pristine condition. To enter the restricted access area, we had to put on white cleanroom "bunny" suits, hats, gloves, and shoe covers. We then took a one-minute air shower, where filtered air was blown across our bodies from top to bottom.

Herb in bunny suit viewing Moon rocks in the Lunar Sample lab at JSC

Moon rocks in the Lunar Sample lab at JSC

A "Lunar Trash Only" container in the lunar sample lab

One of the most unusual pieces of equipment I noticed in the lab was a closed container labeled "Lunar Trash Only." I've often wondered what would fit the definition of lunar trash but I was afraid to open the lid.

* * *

A few months before I retired, Vickie Kloeris, the ISS food system manager, and I were profiled in the JSC Roundup publication in a feature called "Humans of JSC." The feature was started by Ellen Ochoa while she was the center director.

It features stories about various people who work at JSC, their jobs, why they enjoy them, and how their roles fit into the overall mission. She wanted to put a focus on mission support workers who are generally always working behind the scenes.

* * *

My final full week as a NASA employee was from December 26 to December 30, 2016. As usual, during the week between Christmas and New Year's Day, there was relatively little work to do, as most employees were on vacation. Since I had to turn in my NASA badge on my last day, January 3, and would lose the ability to bring visitors on-site or access the places they enjoyed seeing (e.g., Mission Control, NBL, and the Space Vehicle Mockup Facility), I spent most of that final week giving tours to friends who wanted to fit in one last visit. On my last day, I also walked slowly through all of those places by myself, taking a few photos, thinking it might be the last time I would be in those places.

As I cleaned out my office and carried the last box of personal items to my car, I bumped into astronaut Chris Cassidy in Building 1 and spoke with him briefly. After turning in my office keys and then my badge at the Badging Office, I drove home feeling a bit sad about leaving but thankful, and even proud, that I had been able to work for so long at such a wonderful place.

I realized how lucky I was to get up every morning and look forward to going to work (almost) every day. Whenever I was walking around the JSC campus and saw one of the Space Center Houston trams full of visitors, I would think to myself, "Wow. They're paying me to come here every day and those people were willing to pay their own money just to get a glimpse of this place."

On my last day of work, I submitted my application to join the NASA Alumni League-JSC.

25 - A Busy Retirement

"Retire from work, but not from life."

-M. K. Soni

As much as I was looking forward to retirement, I knew I would miss my job at NASA—the people, the daily challenges, the feeling of contributing to our space program, and showing visitors the amazing facilities at JSC. I never considered going to work for a NASA contractor after retiring, but I intended to stay closely connected to NASA and the space program. It has been a huge part of my life since I was 11 years old, and it will continue to be.

I wasn't sure what to expect in retirement, but I felt that being active in the NASA Alumni League would be an effective way to stay connected to what was going on at JSC. I wanted to have time to volunteer for nonprofit organizations connected to the space program, like Space Center Houston and the Astronaut Scholarship Foundation. I also wanted to become involved in community theater again with the Clear Creek Community Theatre (where I would eventually perform and serve on the theater's Board of Directors).

* * *

Five days after retiring, I applied to attend a NASA Social planned for February 1 at JSC to coincide with Super Bowl 51 being played in Houston on February 5. Those selected to attend a NASA Social are given the same type of access to NASA personnel and facilities as traditional news media outlets. They may view launches, participate in media briefings, and take tours, among other opportunities, but attendees are responsible for their own transportation, lodging, and meals.

Because NASA is hoping to reach a unique audience, separate and distinct from traditional audiences, NASA employees are not allowed to apply. Since retiring, I've now attended three NASA Socials and have seen authors, lawyers, stand-up comedians, psychologists, TV meteorologists, museum curators, artists, and a pro football player (former Indianapolis Colt and Baltimore Raven, Tony Siragusa) selected for NASA Socials.

Ten days after applying for the so-called "Space Bowl" NASA Social, I was informed that I had been put on the waitlist. That was not a surprise, since being a former NASA employee was likely a strike against me. I clearly did not fit into the nontraditional journalist category they were ideally looking for, but I thought that it was worth a shot. To my surprise, I was informed just five days before the event that I had been moved off the waitlist and selected as a participant.

I would learn later that, since the original selections had been announced just 12 days before the event, many of those selected who did not live in Houston were unable to make flight, hotel, or rental car reservations due to the demand from visitors coming to Houston for the Super Bowl. Since I lived here, transportation and lodging were not a problem for me. I'm convinced that's why I was moved from the waitlist.

When we arrived at Space Center Houston the morning of the event to sign in and receive our credentials, we were told we would meet in the IMAX theater, where we would have a live linkup on the big screen with astronauts Peggy Whitson and Shane Kimbrough on the ISS.

There was a stack of index cards on the desk, and we were told that if we wanted to ask Peggy and Shane a question, we could write it on a card and the best ten questions would be chosen.

I was aware that the Bigelow Expandable Activity Module (BEAM) had been docked with the ISS several months earlier, so I wrote the question, "Have you entered the BEAM since it was expanded, and how is it performing so far?" The BEAM was a human-rated expandable habitat for use in low-Earth orbit made by Bigelow Aerospace. It was docked to the ISS for a two-year test period and closed off to the rest of the ISS. Astronauts would enter the BEAM and collect pressure and temperature data and check its structural stability.

Peggy Whitson and Shane Kimbrough on the IMAX theater screen at Space Center Houston on a live hookup with the ISS during the NASA Social

I was thrilled to learn that my question was one of those selected. That was quite an experience, talking to astronauts while looking up at a 50-foot tall live video of them in space.

Peggy Whitson answered my question saying that Jeff Williams had been the first to go inside the BEAM a few months earlier. He collected air samples, retrieved several data sensors, and installed ducting to help with air circulation. He also checked to make sure all of the air had been released from the tanks that had been used for pressurization. He later installed sensors to gather data on how it was reacting to radiation and orbital debris. Whitson said that the BEAM was performing very well.

Bigelow Aerospace ceased operations in March 2020 and transferred ownership of the module to NASA. The original agreement with Bigelow was to keep the BEAM on the ISS for two years and then jettison it. Since it had exceeded expectations, NASA kept the BEAM docked to the ISS to use as additional cargo storage space and as a testbed for new technology demonstrations.

NASA Social group with astronaut Doug "Wheels" Wheelock in the Apollo Mission Operations Control room during the "Space Bowl" NASA Social.

From Apollo To Artemis

The remainder of the day was spent hanging out with astronaut Doug Wheelock in the Apollo Mission Operations Control Room and visiting both the Space Vehicle Mockup Facility and the NBL. There, astronaut Vic Glover, who played football for Cal Poly (and was recently selected as an Artemis II crew member), explained how a football uniform and helmet are similar to a spacesuit in how they protect the wearer.

We were also given a guided tour of Space Center Houston. That was interesting because I seemed to know more about some of their exhibits than the young man guiding our tour. When I returned home that evening, I received an email from Space Center Houston asking if I would be interested in becoming a volunteer. I considered that offer, but I felt that the requirement for a minimum of 12 volunteer hours per month was too much of a commitment at that time.

One of the benefits of being a volunteer was free admission, but I already enjoyed that benefit as a NASA Alumni League member. Two years later, SCH lowered the volunteer requirement to a minimum of five hours per month and I accepted that offer. Unfortunately, the pandemic struck eight months later, and I ceased that volunteer activity.

* * *

While working with Flight Operations, I became friends with Mike Fossum, who flew to space three times, performed seven spacewalks, and was an ISS Commander during his last mission. He was also the first Texas A&M undergraduate to fly to space. (Mike and I were both born in South Dakota.) Two weeks after I retired, I attended Mike's retirement party, where three of his former crewmates—Chris Cassidy, Stephanie Wilson, and Dan Burbank—told great stories about flying with him.

281

Herb with astronaut Mike Fossum

Mike is now a vice president at Texas A&M, the Chief Operating Officer of the Texas A&M Galveston Campus, and the Superintendent of the A&M Maritime Academy. I often see him at ceremonies in the Astronaut Memorial Grove.

* * *

Ellen Ochoa retired in May 2018 after a 28-year career with NASA. She served as the JSC Director over her final 5 years at NASA. The NASA beat reporter for the Houston Chronicle, Alex Stuckey, asked me for a quote about Ellen for her news story about Ellen's retirement. In her published story, she included my quote: "I think the world of her. She's accessible and she's smart—no surprise there—and she cared deeply about the people who worked at Johnson."

I attended Ellen's retirement celebration at Space Center Houston shortly thereafter. The most poignant moment of the retirement celebration was when Ellen started telling stories about some of the cards and letters she had received from people whose lives she had touched, thanking her for her inspiration and kindness. By the end of her speech, not only was Ellen in tears, most of the attendees were as well.

* * *

*Herb with former University of Texas and pro football player
Quan Cosby at Space Center Houston*

As a UT alum and a huge college football fan, I had become friends with one of the Longhorns' former wide receivers, Quan Cosby, who played pro football with the Bengals, Broncos, Colts, and Jaguars from 2009 to 2012. In March, he asked if I could give him and his family a tour of NASA. I told him he was a few months late for that, but I would be happy to give them a personal tour of Space Center Houston, which was the next best thing.

We had a wonderful time that day, and I got a photo with Quan in front of the Shuttle *Independence*, flashing our "Hook 'Em Horns" hand sign. It turned out to be the first of many personal tours of SCH that I've given to friends and family who asked for a tour of "NASA."

* * *

In June, I attended a Data Science Conference at JSC with several Datanaut friends: Karen Lopez, Cindy Chin, Noemi Derzsy, and Victoria Rutledge. Datanauts is a year-round program for members from around the world to learn how to use NASA's open data and practice data science skills. The program is open to anyone interested in technology, data science, and space.

The speakers were astronaut Jeff Williams and Lisa Vaughn, a Houston meteorologist with a background in math, statistics, and coding. After Williams finished speaking, our group took a photo with him.

L to R – Karen Lopez, Noemi Derzsy, Jeff Williams, Victoria Rutledge, Herb, & Cindy Chin at NASA's Data Science Conference in 2017

* * *

Shortly thereafter, I was asked again to help with a tour of SCH. One of my NASA friends and co-workers, Stacey

Nakamura, was the president of the MIT Club of South Texas and was hosting the MIT Club of Mexico for a visit. Stacey asked me to help guide the tour of about 30 people, a fairly large group. A few years earlier, I had accepted Stacey's suggestion to join the local MIT Club because my older son and his wife are MIT alumni.

It was a memorable day, showing the visitors from Mexico the Apollo 17 Command Module, the Apollo Mission Operations Control Room, the Shuttle *Independence* exhibit, the Saturn V at Rocket Park, and everything else SCH had to offer.

The day was topped off with dinner at Frenchie's restaurant, a local favorite among astronauts and other NASA employees. Stacey had not made it public that he had been battling cancer for some time. He lost his battle just over two years later. I'm grateful that I could spend that day with him.

* * *

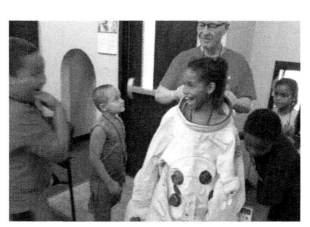

Space Camp attendees trying on the mockup Apollo spacesuit

In August, I was invited by my friend Kia McClain to be the featured guest at a week-long Exploration Mars Space Camp in Topeka, Kansas, for underprivileged kids. I checked out an Apollo spacesuit mockup with helmet and gloves and a

Shuttle food tray of freeze-dried food from the JSC Exhibits office for the trip and spent the week speaking to over 100 young kids about NASA and space exploration.

The kids especially loved trying on the spacesuit. The program was part of Topeka's Neighborhood Opportunity for Wellness program sponsored by the United Way.

Herb wearing Joe Mays' Houston Texans jersey at Space Camp

Former pro football player Joe Mays, who played linebacker for the Eagles, Broncos, Texans, Chiefs, and Chargers from 2008 to 2015, was also a guest speaker at the space camp. I enjoyed spending time with Joe and his wife LaToyia. Joe brought four of his former teams' jerseys with him, and he told me, "If you let me wear your NASA T-shirt, I'll let you wear my Texans jersey."

I will admit that the Texans jersey looks better on him than on me.

* * *

EXPLORATION MARS SPACE CAMP

Imaginations take flight

Herb Baker, who retired after a 42-year career at NASA, mostly working in operations support at the Johnson Space Center, joined Topeka campers at the Exploration Mars Space Camp this week to share his experiences at the federal agency.

Topeka children meet NASA professional at Mars Space Camp

By Morgan Chilson
morgan.chilson@cjonline.com

The open-mouthed "wow factor" that space travel creates was brought to children in East Topeka this week as part of a Space Camp that included meeting NASA professional Herb Baker and former NFL football player Joe Mays.

Kia McClain, a Topekan chosen last year to be a social media influencer for NASA's Mars journey, reached out to the Neighborhood Opportu-

nity for Wellness program to bring the space event to the Highland Park neighborhoods.

More than 100 kids showed up from the NOW initiative neighborhoods at Deer Creek, Pine Ridge Manor and Echo Ridge when the camp started this week, McClain said.

"My favorite part of camp has been trying on the space outfit from the astronaut that came out," camper LaDaysha Baird said. "I like to dress up."

SPACE continues on 7A

Campers visit with Star Wars characters prior to presentations on Friday, the final day of the Exploration Mars Space Camp, at Deer Creek Community Center.

At the end of the week, the Topeka Capital-Journal featured a photo of me on its front page with a story about the space camp. It was the first and only time I've been on the front page of a newspaper, which is probably fortunate.

My friend, Tim Gagnon, better known as "The Patch Guy," designed and produced a special patch for that space camp on short notice. Thanks to Tim, we were able to give every kid attending the camp a patch. Tim is an artist who has been designing and creating cloth patches for NASA, as well as many other groups since he designed the patch for the ISS Expedition 11 mission. When Tim was invited by astronaut Eric Boe to design the STS-126 mission patch in 2008, he invited his friend, Dr. Jorge Cartes of Madrid, Spain, to join him on the project. Tim and Jorge have collaborated on patches for many other Shuttle missions and ISS Expeditions since that time.

* * *

Herb with astronaut Jasmin Moghbeli at Ellington Field during an FOD Fajita Festival

Even though I was retired, I was invited to the annual FOD Fajita Festival in October. As always, it was in a large hangar at Ellington Field. This one was memorable because I got to hang out with astronaut Jasmin Moghbeli. She participates in many outreach activities for NASA, so I've been able to talk with her at several NASA events. She was the commander for the SpaceX Crew-7 mission to the ISS in August 2023, her first spaceflight.

I also talked with astronaut Reid Wiseman, who will be the commander for the Artemis II mission. Astronaut Jessica Meir was working the margarita machine that evening, so I visited with her several times. At that point, she had not yet been assigned to a mission, so I wished her luck on getting a flight assignment.

Her first flight came 23 months later as part of the ISS Expedition 61/62 crew. It was on that mission that she participated in the first all-female spacewalk with crewmate Christina Koch.

* * *

In August 2017, Hurricane Harvey hit Texas and Louisiana and caused massive flooding in the Houston area. It was the costliest natural disaster recorded in Texas at the time. Nine months later, there were still areas where carpet, furniture, drywall, and other items ruined by the rising water were piled on the sides of the streets, waiting to be picked up and carried away.

One of those communities was Dickinson, TX, a few miles south of JSC and home to Gene Kranz, whose house had been damaged by the floodwaters. The junior high school in Dickinson is named after Gene.

I was recruited by a member of Team Rubicon, a disaster response team, to help them remove most of that debris along the streets and roadways in Dickinson on a Saturday in May 2018. When Gene learned of Team Rubicon's efforts, he offered to have dinner with us and speak to the volunteers that evening at the church he attends in Dickinson.

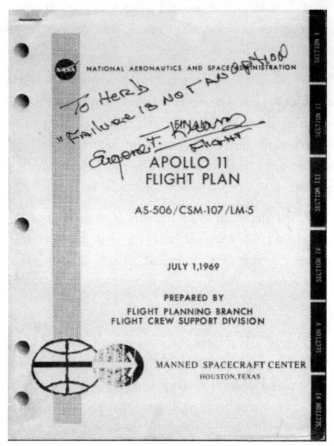

Apollo 11 Flight Plan from 1969 signed by Gene Kranz

Gene was the Flight Director in Mission Control when Apollo 11 landed on the Moon. One of my prized mementos from covering that mission with the news media is an original Apollo 11 Flight Plan that I had picked up from the Public Affairs Office. I took it to the church that evening and Gene signed it for me on the cover with the inscription, "Failure is not an option—Eugene F. Kranz, Flight." There were about 20 people there that evening and he was signing anything they asked. One woman asked him to sign the back of the T-shirt she was wearing, which he happily did.

Herb with Gene Kranz in his hometown of Dickinson, TX

After dinner, Gene told stories about every Apollo mission from Apollo 10 through Apollo 17 and then talked about some of the activities he was involved in after retiring from NASA in 1994. He said he would speak at air shows and his "price" was to ride with the Blue Angels and Thunderbirds while they were doing their pre-show rehearsals. He also built an aerobatic biplane in his garage, but it was destroyed in a hurricane (he didn't say which one). After writing his first book, *Failure is not an Option*, he joined the military speaking circuit. He said he had spoken to more than 100 military units.

* * *

In July 2018, I attended Spacefest IX in Tucson, AZ. Spacefest was an annual three-day event held in Tucson, AZ, that featured Gemini, Apollo, and Shuttle astronauts, along with space historians, authors, artists, and other guest speakers.

The event featured lunches and dinners with the astronauts, as well as a cocktail party. There was an astronaut autograph show, book signings, and photo opportunities, as well as several panels of astronauts, flight directors, and other space dignitaries and scientists. The four-day event was the largest collection of astronauts and astronaut family members I've ever attended.

Herb with Tess Simpson and Dee O'Hara at Spacefest in 2018

I met Dee O'Hara at Spacefest IX. She tells a funny story about how she was chosen to become the nurse for the Mercury 7 astronauts. After graduating from high school, she wanted to become a nurse. She joined the Air Force and went to officer's training at Maxwell Air Force Base in Alabama. She was then sent to Patrick Air Force Base at Cape Canaveral, Florida in May 1959.

She was working in the labor and delivery room at the hospital there when she received a message that "the old man," meaning the commander of the hospital, wanted to see her the next day. This is an excerpt from her story in the JSC Oral History Project:

"I was terrified, because I'd only been there six months and I knew that when you went to see Colonel

Knauf, it was for two reasons: one, you were in trouble; or, two, it was for a promotion. Well, I knew it was not for a promotion because I'd only been there six months. So I kept thinking, oh, boy, what have I done? I didn't remember harming anybody or harming a baby.

I gave morning report the next morning and went to his office, and here sat his exec officer, the chief nurse, and all these people. I really was terrified because I didn't know why exactly I was there. I literally sat on the edge of the seat. Anyway, he started talking about Mercury, and I thought, well, there's a planet Mercury and there's mercury in a thermometer, and then he mentioned astronauts. That, of course, didn't mean anything to me. I didn't know what they were. He mentioned NASA, and I thought he was saying Nassau, because of the island of Nassau. I had just been there, and I thought, 'How did the heck did he know I was down there?' Anyway, I was quite confused.

He turned and said to me, 'Well, do you want the job?' I kind of turned around, because I didn't think he was talking to me. He said, 'Well, you haven't heard a word I've said, have you?' I said, 'No, sir.' And he said, 'Well, do you want the job or not?'

I didn't know what else to say, so I said, 'Well, I guess so,' absolutely not knowing at all what I had committed myself to. Of course, the chief nurse, who was there, was furious with me afterwards, because she was losing me out of the hospital. Also, she thought NASA was crazy because they were going to be putting a man on top of a rocket.

Anyway, that's how it started. So in January of 1960, I went out to Cape Canaveral, as it was known then, and set up the aeromed lab. It was the beginning, and that's how it happened."

In addition to meeting Dee, highlights of the Spacefest event for me included meeting Emily Carney, the founder of the Facebook group Space Hipsters, which now has more than 62,000 members (of which I am one), having lunch with astronauts Anna Fisher and Rhea Seddon, talking with astronaut friends Fred Haise, Jack Lousma, and Clay Anderson, and seeing a sneak preview of the film *Searching for Skylab*, which would premiere at the U.S. Space and Rocket Center seven months later.

I also got to speak with Rick Armstrong, Marie Fullerton (Gordon Fullerton's widow), seamstress Jean Wright, and former Flight Director Milt Heflin, among others, while there.

The event was run by Kelsey Poor of Novaspace, which her late father, Kim Poor, had started. Sadly for all of us space exploration enthusiasts, the Spacefest events were discontinued after 2021, due to the COVID-19 pandemic.

Herb (at far left on top row) with Clay Anderson and other astronauts, flight controllers, and their family members attending Spacefest IX in 2018

* * *

It was during this period that the Education Department at Space Center Houston contacted me about speaking at various events. I was first asked to speak with a group of international students as part of its Space Center University (Space Center U) program.

Herb speaking to students at Space Center Houston

I've spoken to Space Center U groups several times since, most recently with a group of high school students from Australia and New Zealand. Space Center U is a multi-day program offered to individuals and groups from around the world that promotes teamwork, problem-solving, communication, and engineering solutions that are applied to space-related situations.

* * *

One of the slides in my presentation to Space Center U students is a summary of American and Russian spaceflight traditions and superstitions. It's an interesting assortment that includes this tradition: If you're an astronaut or a cosmonaut launching into space from the Baikonur Cosmodrome in

Kazakhstan, you will stop to pee on the right rear tire of your bus on the 20-minute drive to the Cosmodrome from the Cosmonaut, Hotel where you've been staying.

This tradition dates back to Soviet cosmonaut Yuri Gagarin, the first person to launch to space in 1961. On the way to the launch pad, Gagarin realized that once he arrived at the launch pad and entered the capsule, his spacesuit would be zipped up and he would be unable to pee for several hours, so he wanted to 'take a leak.' Since that time, all male crew members have followed this tradition.

They exit the bus that is transferring them to the launch site and stand at the right rear wheel of the bus to relieve themselves, just as Gagarin did. Women astronauts and cosmonauts have the option of peeing in a cup in advance and splashing it on the wheel when the bus stops.

* * *

In August 2018, I learned that the Astronaut Scholarship Foundation (ASF) would be holding its annual Space Rendezvous event in Houston that fall. The ASF is located in Orlando, FL, and most of their events are at or near the Kennedy Space Center.

The Astronaut Scholarship Foundation was founded by six of the Mercury 7 astronauts, Betty Grissom (widow of Gus Grissom, the seventh astronaut), and two others.

Its mission is to help the U.S. maintain its leadership in technology and innovation by supporting student scholars in STEM. The ASF awards merit-based scholarships to undergraduate juniors and seniors studying in STEM fields. ASF also provides the students with mentors and networking with astronauts and industry leaders.

I contacted the ASF and offered to volunteer at the event in Houston that November, as well as at future events. I learned that they were also recruiting mentors for their Astronaut Scholars so I registered as a mentor as well. I've mentored an Astronaut Scholar for the past five years and recently signed up to be a mentor again next year.

The Space Rendezvous was a three-day event that began with an art show and astronaut reception and later included numerous panels, luncheons, a moonlight mixer, book signings, an autograph show, and ended with a gala on Saturday night at Space Center Houston.

One of the panels called, "Transition to Skylab" included astronauts Rusty Schweickart, Jack Lousma, and Vance Brand. Because of my history with the Skylab Program, I was asked to be the moderator for the panel.

L to R – Jack Lousma, Vance Brand, Rusty Schweickart, and Herb (moderating the panel)

I had a few prepared questions for the panel, but once those three guys started telling stories about their involvement in Skylab, there was little moderating required, and I hardly had a chance to ask any of the prepared questions. Rusty Schweickart was especially animated and was on a roll that day.

The panel was scheduled to end at noon, but when noon came, the panelists were still having a great time, and none of the audience members were leaving. Rusty leaned over and asked me if it was OK to tell one more story. I told him, "Go for it!" We finally broke for lunch about 15 to 20 minutes later.

Another panel featured several Apollo-era flight controllers, including Jerry Bostick, Bill Moon, John Aaron, and Ed Fendell, and several others.

L to R – Apollo flight controllers Jerry Bostick, Bill Moon, Herb, John Aaron, and Ed Fendell

The ASF's primary need for volunteers for the Space Rendezvous event was for help at the astronaut autograph and memorabilia show, an all-day event held at the Lone Star Flight Museum at Ellington Airport, not far from JSC. Each volunteer was paired with one of the approximately 25 astronauts and flight directors at the show to handle payment transactions for autographs.

I was lucky enough to be paired with astronaut Nicole Stott. Spending eight hours with Nicole that day, talking about spaceflight and her artwork, was incredible. I'm happy to say that our paths have crossed several times since that day.

Herb with Nicole Stott after the autograph show at the ASF Space Rendezvous event

With my connections to aerospace companies in the local JSC area, I was able to introduce the ASF's Donor Relations Manager, Krissy Stewart, to leaders of many of those companies. Krissy traveled to Houston in October, and we spent two days going from one company to another, telling them about the ASF and discussing potential collaboration opportunities.

* * *

In February 2019, I attended my first Space Exploration Educators Conference (SEEC), an annual event held at Space Center Houston for educators from around the world that has been held annually since 1995. The event is primarily for K-12 classroom teachers, but those of us who speak to students without being classroom teachers are also eligible to attend as "informal educators."

The three-day (Thursday–Saturday) conference is a professional development experience that includes hands-on workshops, keynote speakers, tours of NASA facilities, and sessions with educators and NASA experts, where innovative and immersive lessons for all grade levels are shared.

It's a wonderful opportunity to network and make connections with 500 to 600 fellow educators. The closing Saturday evening banquets are "out of this world." The astronaut band Bandella, led by Chris Hadfield, provided the entertainment for the banquet in 2020.

* * *

In July 2019, during the 50th anniversary of Apollo 11, JSC held an Apollo 11 Memorabilia Event at the Gilruth Center. Employees and retirees were invited to bring items that either they or their parents had collected from the Apollo era for a Show and Tell.

Herb talking with visitors viewing his collection of Apollo memorabilia at JSC celebrating the 50th anniversary of Apollo 11

I have a large collection of Apollo memorabilia, so I registered for a display table. Luckily, the person assigned the table next to mine didn't show up, allowing me to spread my collection across two tables—though I still didn't have enough room to display all of it.

I enjoyed talking with the younger NASA employees who had not seen most of the items I was displaying. Two young engineers, who happened to be working on a Mars rover, were fascinated by a booklet I had describing the Lunar Roving Vehicle in detail. They gave me their email addresses and asked me to make a PDF copy of the booklet and send it to them.

* * *

The Association of Space Explorers (ASE) held its annual Planetary Congress in Houston in October 2019. The ASE is a non-profit organization with a membership composed of people who have completed at least one Earth orbit in space— 62 miles above Earth's sea level, as defined by the Fédération Aéronautique Internationale—and is the only professional association for astronauts.

The ASE was founded in 1985 by astronauts Rusty Schweickart and Loren Acton, and cosmonauts Alexei Leonov, Vitaly Sevastyanov, and Georgi Grechko. The ASE has over 400 members from 37 different countries. The ASE's Planetary Congress is attended by member astronauts and cosmonauts from around the world.

The location of the annual ASE Planetary Congress rotates between different countries every year. The conference includes technical sessions covering updates and future plans for human activities in space during the week-long event.

More than 120 astronauts and cosmonauts from 19 countries attended the 2019 Congress in Houston, which was officially hosted by retired astronaut Bonnie Dunbar. It's traditional for the astronauts and cosmonauts to spend one day visiting schools, aerospace companies, and scientific institutions, talking with students, teachers, and community leaders.

I was not eligible to attend the Congress itself, of course, but I volunteered, along with several other NASA Alumni League members to serve as escorts and provide local transportation for the ASE delegates to the schools they visited on their Community Day.

I was lucky enough to be paired with Loren Acton, one of the ASE's founding members and a solar x-ray physicist, who flew as a payload specialist on STS-51-F in July 1985.

Our first stop that day was St. Anne Catholic School in Houston. When we arrived, Acton spoke to an excited crowd of about 100 young students, talking about his Shuttle flight, showing photos from his mission, and answering questions. We were there for approximately two hours and then stopped at a nearby restaurant to have lunch before traveling to our second stop for the day.

During lunch, I mentioned that I would be performing in a theater production that was opening in two days. I was playing the role of Mycroft Holmes, Sherlock's older brother, in a show called "*Sherlock Holmes and the Adventures of the Suicide Club*" at the Clear Creek Community Theatre across the street from JSC. Acton said, "My wife and I love theater! We recently moved from Montana to Reno, Nevada, and one of the first things we did when we arrived in Reno was look for a local theater."

Our theater was doing a matinée performance that Sunday, and since Acton and his wife were staying in Houston for the weekend, he said they would plan to attend.

Shuttle astronaut Loren Acton with students at St. Anne Catholic School

After lunch, we drove to our second destination, the Energy Institute High School, the first high school in the U.S. devoted to preparing students for careers in the energy sector. Every subject taught in the school includes topics related to energy.

The school follows a project-based learning model, meaning it relies more heavily on group projects and less on standardized testing. These high school students were older than those at our previous stop and showed great interest in the solar experiments Acton had conducted during his Shuttle mission.

When I volunteered to be an escort for one of the ASE members on their Community Day, I had no idea with whom I would be paired. Looking back, there's no one I would have been happier to spend that day with than Loren Acton.

One interesting fact about Acton's STS-51-F mission on *Challenger* is that it was the Shuttle flight during which Coca-

Cola and Pepsi were tested against each other. He told me that often, when he gave speeches, audiences were more interested in hearing about the Coke/Pepsi experiment than about solar physics.

Loren and his wife, Evelyn, did make it to see our theater performance that weekend. They were kind enough to hang around in the lobby after the show, talking and taking photos with me and some of our show's other cast members.

Herb with Evelyn and Loren Acton at Clear Creek Community Theatre

* * *

In October 2019, the NASA Alumni League announced an opportunity to volunteer for Girlstart, a nonprofit STEM organization headquartered in Austin, TX. Girlstart designs and conducts year-round STEM education programs for K-12 girls, encouraging an interest in STEM majors and careers.

Girlstart hosted its second annual Girls in STEM Conference at a Houston high school. I volunteered at the STEM Conference that day along with three other NASA

Alumni League members—Jeff Davis, Beth Fischer, and Cindy Draughon.

More than 250 fourth- through eighth-grade girls from the Houston area attended the event. Throughout the day, they attended hands-on workshops led by women from organizations such as: NASA, ExxonMobil, Jacobs Technologies, Shell, and many others. Seeing the girls' interest and enthusiasm, while learning about STEM, made the day immensely rewarding.

I continue to volunteer for Girlstart events in the Houston area, and I currently serve as the Alumni League sponsor for Girlstart, one of several nonprofit organizations promoting STEM education to which the Alumni League makes donations.

* * *

In November 2019, Nicole Stott narrated a documentary podcast for the British Broadcasting Corporation (BBC) titled "Hey Sisters, Sew Sisters." The subject of the documentary was the seamstresses who sewed soft goods for spacesuits and spacecraft throughout the Apollo, Skylab, and Shuttle Programs.

For Apollo, Nicole interviewed two women, Joanne Thompson and Jeanne Wilson, who had sewn the Apollo spacesuits while working at the International Latex Corporation.

Nicole interviewed me for the podcast to tell Mom's story about the Skylab parasol. She also interviewed Jean Wright to talk about her work as a seamstress on the Space Shuttle Thermal Protection System. The podcast was published on the BBC website in December 2019.

* * *

In mid-November, NASA announced that it was planning an "Artemis Day" NASA Social event for December. The first day would be spent at NASA's Michoud Assembly Facility (MAF) in New Orleans, LA, and the second day would be spent touring the Stennis Space Center, 40 miles east of the MAF in Mississippi.

At the MAF, attendees would see the Space Launch System (SLS) rocket core stage assembled with all four RS-25 engines, that would fly on the Artemis I mission. Attendees would also hear from NASA Administrator Jim Bridenstine and others about progress being made on the Artemis program and tour the MAF facility.

Herb with the STS rocket core stage assembly at the Michoud Assembly Facility in New Orleans, LA

On the following day, attendees would tour the Stennis Space Center where the rocket's core stage would go for testing before being shipped to the Kennedy Space Center for the uncrewed Artemis I launch with the Orion spacecraft. Approximately 50 active social media users would be selected to attend the event and be given the same access as the news media.

After enjoying my first NASA Social in 2017, I applied for the Artemis Day NASA Social and was pleasantly surprised to be selected. This event turned out to be even more fun and memorable than the first one I attended.

In all of my years at NASA, I had not had an opportunity to visit the MAF, so I enjoyed finally seeing that huge rocket-building facility where the Shuttle's external tanks had been built. I also met and talked briefly with NASA Administrator Jim Bridenstine and renewed my acquaintance with Jasmin Moghbeli, who was also at the MAF that day.

Traffic sign near Infinity Science Center in Mississippi

The next day, we met at the Infinity Science Center in Mississippi just a few miles from Stennis. We noticed a helpful traffic sign showing the way to Infinity—or Beyond.

Fred Haise is a passionate supporter of the Infinity Science Center, not far from where he grew up in Biloxi, MS. The Science Center, which is affiliated with the Stennis Space Center, includes memorabilia from Fred's astronaut career. It opened in 2012.

At Stennis, we saw rocket engines being built at the Aerojet Rocketdyne facility there, and visited the huge B-2 Test Stand, where the SLS core stage would be tested. The nearby historic A-1 Test Stand at Stennis was designated the Fred Haise Test Stand in his honor in March 2020.

Group photo of the Artemis Day NASA Social attendees at the B-2 Test Stand at Stennis Space Center where the SLS engines would later be tested

The best part of this NASA Social, however, was becoming friends with several of the other attendees in our group. In the four years since the Social, we've had several Zoom meetings to catch up on what everyone's doing and have stayed in close touch through our social media accounts.

It's a very diverse and talented group, including Dr. Jennifer Ferguson (a neuroscientist & psychologist); Emily Olsen (a science & pop culture cataloguer at Sotheby's); Grant A. Harkness (a nuclear maintenance supervisor and Founder of Wilton Observatory); Amy Ely (a Director of STEM at Detroit Catholic Central High School and a Modern Space Education advocate/presenter); Maria Schwartzman Webb (an instructor of computer science); and Michael Schoenewies, a photographer & UX designer who also does 3D scanning/caving with CAIRN (Cave Archaeology Investigation & Research Network).

Others in the group include "Ellie" Elysium Biddle (a U.S. Military academy graduate and an Officer assigned to U.S. Army Pacific's 1st Multi-Domain Task Force) and Michele O'Shaughnessy (an engineer and project manager who is actively involved with the Space Camp Alumni Association Board and is a former Board Director for the Society of Women Engineers). We have so much to talk about that some of our Zoom sessions have lasted longer than three hours.

* * *

In late November, my friend Tara Foster, who lives in Australia but has visited Ireland several times, made me aware of a six-year-old Irish boy who dreamed of being a Capcom for NASA and who has a rare lifelong genetic condition affecting his bones and connective tissue called osteogenesis imperfecta.

The young boy, Adam King, had become well known after appearing on an episode of Ireland's "Late Late Toy Show," the world's second-longest-running late-night talk show, after "The

Tonight Show." His heartwarming appearance on the show went viral, and he stole the hearts of all those who watched it with his smile, determination, and positive attitude.

I tweeted a message to Adam on Twitter, which was seen by Sarah Poole, a producer for the BBC in the U.K., who reached out to me and asked if I would record a short 30-second video for Adam. I recorded the video telling Adam that I would love to see him at NASA someday, wishing him all the best, and telling him to keep dreaming big. The video was broadcast on the BBC Breakfast show the next morning.

Adam's appearance on the "Late Late Toy Show" also caught the attention of Canadian astronaut Chris Hadfield, who talked with Adam remotely and sent him autographed photos. NASA even joined in and tweeted, "There's space for everybody at NASA, and we can't wait for Adam to one day join our team of dreamers. We'll be here when he's ready."

* * *

If you're still reading this book, interested in space exploration, and have a Facebook account, you might enjoy the public group called Space Hipsters. The membership includes retired astronauts and some of their family members, many other current and former NASA and commercial space industry professionals, authors, artists, educators, and others who are simply space enthusiasts.

Most importantly, the group is well-moderated. The group also has its own logo (and button), organizes group field trips to locations of interest to space enthusiasts, holds online/virtual events, and generously contributes to good causes such as the nonprofit Taking Up Space, a Space Hipsters favorite.

Taking Up Space (taking-up-space.org) was founded by Czarina Salido in 2016 and is dedicated to decreasing the gender gap in STEM fields, focusing on middle-school-aged Native American girls. The organization provides a 16-week colloquium on the fundamentals of aerospace, body positivity, and Native American arts and culture, culminating in a trip to NASA's Space Camp at the U.S. Space & Rocket Center in Huntsville, AL.

Herb wearing his Space Hipster button during a panel conversation with Rusty Schweickart

26 - NASA Alumni League Board of Directors

Shortly after joining the NASA Alumni League-JSC (NAL-JSC), I became a lifetime member. In addition to remaining connected with NASA, the Alumni League offers at least two benefits: an Alumni League ID badge that allows me 24/7 access to the JSC site and free admission to Space Center Houston. Unlike the NASA employee badge I had to give up when I retired, my Alumni League badge unfortunately does not allow me to bring anyone on-site with me when I enter JSC.

JSC and KSC are the only two NASA centers that have NASA Alumni League organizations. Three other centers—Marshall Space Flight Center, Goddard Space Flight Center, and Langley Research Center—have retiree/alumni associations, but they are not officially part of the NASA Alumni League. To become a member of NAL-JSC, one must have been an employee of either JSC or the Jet Propulsion Laboratory (JPL) for at least one year.

Former employees of another federal government agency who served an extended detail assignment at JSC for one year or longer or other persons employed by NASA as a "Special Employee" to complete a special assignment at JSC lasting one year or more are also eligible for membership in our Chapter.

We currently have over 700 members, including at least 16 astronauts, as well as flight directors/flight controllers, engineers, and members from many other NASA career fields.

Our vision is to support the U.S. space program with technical knowledge, historical preservation, educational outreach, and provide financial support to organizations supporting STEM education. During the current year, we have donated over $25,000 to local school districts and nonprofit organizations supporting STEM.

We support an archive collection at the nearby University of Houston-Clear Lake to preserve JSC's historical documents and we host a monthly program in which speakers discuss topics of interest in the world of space exploration. We also have regular social events.

I was not on the NAL-JSC Board of Directors for the first three years after retiring, but in 2020, the incumbent board secretary asked me if I would be interested in running for that position because she wanted to serve in a different role. The chapter president at the time was astronaut Bill McArthur, with whom I had worked closely at JSC, so it was a fortunate opportunity for me. I was elected Secretary in the summer of 2020 and have been in that position since.

* * *

In April 2022, I attended the Astronaut Scholarship Foundation's Apollo 16 50th Anniversary Celebration at the Marriott Marquis Hotel in downtown Houston. There was a panel discussion including Charlie Duke, Fred Haise, and Tony England (Apollo 16 EVA Capcom), moderated by former NASA Public Affairs Officer Doug Ward.

For the gala, I was lucky enough to be seated with several of my ASF friends, including Caroline Schumacher (president and CEO) and Nicole Russ (director of the Scholarship Program). I also visited with Mary Armstrong, who attended the event with her husband, Rick.

Herb with Mary Armstrong at ASF's Apollo 16 Anniversary event

* * *

Mentoring panel at JSC – L to R: Erick Castillon, Ashley Owens, Veronica Clauson, Trinesha Dixon, Herb, and Rob Kelso

I participated in the JSC Mentoring Program for many years while still employed there. After joining the NASA Alumni League, I joined their mentoring committee. Since retiring, I've also annually mentored an Astronaut Scholar for the Astronaut Scholarship Foundation. I enjoy getting to know these amazing students. Spending time with them on a regular basis keeps me feeling young.

In October 2023, I was invited by JSC to join a mentoring panel for a National Mentoring Day event for its employees.

* * *

Being on the NAL-JSC Board of Directors has resulted in several opportunities that I likely would not have had otherwise. One of the organizations we support is the Patricia Huffman Smith NASA Remembering *Columbia* Museum in Hemphill, Texas. The nonprofit museum opened in February 2011 and is located in Sabine County in East Texas, where much of the STS-107 debris was recovered. The remains of all seven *Columbia* astronauts were also recovered in Sabine County. The museum honors the STS-107 crew and all 28 flights of Shuttle *Columbia*, as well as two men who lost their lives in a helicopter accident while supporting the STS-107 recovery effort.

In 2023, on the 20th anniversary of the *Columbia* accident, the museum and NAL-JSC collaborated on a three-day event to honor the mission. The event included an art show, a high school robotics competition, and a memorial service on the morning of February 1. NAL-JSC members conducted three discussion panels in the museum's auditorium that day.

The first panel, "Why is Space Dangerous, Yet So Safe?" was moderated by former Shuttle Business Manager Dorothy Rasco and included former NASA Launch Director Mike Leinbach and astronauts Bill McArthur and Brewster Shaw as panelists.

The second panel, "Making Space for Women," was moderated by our current NAL-JSC president, Estella Gillette, and included NASA Historian and author Jennifer Ross-Nazzal, former JSC Director of Human Resources Natalie Saiz, and aerospace consultant Michele Brekke.

I was the moderator for the third panel, "Making STEM for Everyone," which included former NASA engineers Carolynn Conley, John Saiz, and Frank Hughes.

While preparing for my panel on the subject of STEM, I learned an interesting piece of trivia. The National Science Foundation began using the term SMET as an acronym for science, mathematics, engineering, and technology sometime in the 1990s. Judith Ramaley, who was the director of the foundation's education and human resources organization in 2001, didn't like the sound of the word "SMET," thinking it sounded too much like smut. She suggested changing SMET to STEM. STEM has a much better ring to it and has been used since that time.

Herb moderating "Making STEM for Everyone" panel at the Remembering Columbia Museum in Hemphill, TX

* * *

In October 2023, I was invited by the Remembering *Columbia* Museum to be the guest speaker at its annual Galactic Gala fundraising event held at the VFW Hall in Hemphill. During the *Columbia* recovery effort, the VFW Hall was converted into a dining hall for the search teams involved in the recovery effort. It was a personal honor for me to be asked to speak at that VFW Hall, especially since many of the folks in attendance that evening had been personally involved in the *Columbia* recovery effort 20 years earlier.

A few of the folks associated with the museum whom I've become friends with include Belinda Gay, Marsha Cooper, Vickie Thomas, Kevin Doolin, and Gerry Schumann, most of whom had been involved in the recovery effort. Belinda, the vice president of the museum, Marsha, and Vickie have been instrumental in establishing and operating the museum.

At the time of the accident, Belinda was head of the VFW Women's Auxiliary in Hemphill, and her husband, Roger, was the commander of the Hemphill VFW Post. Belinda walked through the woods with the search teams for several days, then joined her husband at the VFW Hall to help prepare and serve meals to the recovery crews. She also solicited donations for the food and organized the volunteers who served 45,000 to 50,000 meals during the first month after the accident.

Marsha, who worked for the U.S. Forest Service, was on one of the first search teams to go into the forests after the accident. While searching in a field near where the first crew member had been found the day before, she discovered another of the crew members. After informing her line boss about her discovery, she was careful to do so in a way that did not alert the nearby news media crews. I can't imagine the emotions she must have felt after witnessing what she saw that day.

Gerry, KSC's safety manager, who knew the crew and their families, made the trip from Florida to assist in the recovery. He was one of the on-site NASA leaders of the recovery effort and remains supportive of the museum today.

* * *

I hope I'm many years away from living in a nursing home (if ever), but since retiring, I've had an odd connection with them. It started several years ago when I was offered what I thought would be an acting job at a nursing home on the north side of Houston. Seasons Assisted Living was a new facility and they wanted to create some promotional material for advertising. Since this gig had been publicized through a theater/acting service, I assumed they wanted to shoot a commercial.

When we arrived that morning at the beautiful, large house that was being converted to a nursing home, we learned that it was a photo shoot. There was no film or video or lines to learn—just posing for still photos. It was more of a modeling job than an acting job, but for $100/hour for 3 hours, I was not going to complain. I was paired with two women, one of whom was my "nurse." Since that day, I've wanted to add professional model to my résumé—even though it was for just a few hours.

A couple of years later, one of my theater actress friends, Angela Reader, who was the executive director of a nursing home in League City, arranged for me to speak to her residents about NASA. I enjoyed that because I believe it was the first time I had spoken to a group in which everyone in the audience was old enough to witness the Apollo Moon landings. It occurred to me that when I spoke to residents of a nursing home, I was always the youngest person in the room—which is a rare occurrence for me.

A few years after that, Angela had become the director of an assisted living facility adjacent to the Johnson Space Center, where the mother of one of NASA's active astronauts resides. The residents had formed a NASA Club and I was invited to speak to them. As before, I enjoyed speaking to this group that had lived through and seemed to remember many of the events I was discussing.

During a recent week I spent at the Remembering *Columbia* Museum, I was asked to speak to the residents of a nearby nursing home, who were unable to travel to the museum. After I finished speaking, one of the residents asked me, "How old are you?" I told him that I'm 72 years old. He replied, "You're the same age as I am!" It seems that I can no longer count on being the youngest person in the room.

* * *

For me, being active in the NASA Alumni League is the next best thing to working at NASA. I've become friends with many JSC retirees that I was not fortunate enough to know while working there. We have an excellent relationship with center management, with JSC Director Vanessa Wyche often referring to our organization as "the legendary NASA Alumni League."

We hold most of our monthly board meetings in conference rooms on-site at JSC. Our monthly presentations from guest speakers and our social events are held at JSC's Gilruth Recreation Center. Our most recent event was a panel discussion celebrating the 55th anniversary of the Apollo 11 lunar landing that featured Fred Haise, Gene Kranz, and Bill Moon as panelists. For me, it was a no-brainer to become a lifetime NAL-JSC member.

* * *

Having supported Flight Operations for the final 8 years of my career, I recently joined the Manned Spaceflight Operations Association (MSOA), which was established in 2017 to preserve the legacy of those who supported the missions flown from the historic Apollo Mission Operations Control Room.

In October 2021, MSOA was expanded to include all those who operationally supported missions from the JSC Mission Control Centers through the end of the Space Shuttle Program, ending with STS-135. Directors Emeritus of MSOA include Gene Kranz, Fred Haise, Gerry Griffin, "Dutch" von Ehrenfried, and (until his passing in 2021) Glynn Lunney.

We recently held an event at the Lone Star Flight Museum at Ellington Field to celebrate the 55th anniversary of the Apollo 11 lunar landing. I captured a photo of Gene, Fred, and "Dutch," joined by Skylab Flight Director Charlie Harlan and flight controllers Bill Moon and Ed Fendell enjoying the festivities.

MSOA attendees at Apollo 11 55th anniversary celebration - (L to R) Charlie Harlan, Fred Haise, Gene Kranz, "Dutch" von Ehrenfried, Bill Moon, and Ed Fendell

Herb with a mockup of the Orion crew capsule which will carry humans farther than they've ever gone before on the Artemis missions

27 - Artemis Program

Humans haven't left low-Earth orbit since 1972, when Apollo 17 landed on the Moon. With the Artemis Program, NASA plans to return to the Moon and send astronauts to the Moon's south pole, where they believe there is a large amount of water and ice.

The Orion crew capsule is larger than the Apollo capsule and can support four astronauts, rather than the three that the Apollo Command Module could support. I've heard Orion referred to as "Apollo on steroids."

NASA is contracting with commercial companies to build the Human Landing Systems that will carry the astronauts from lunar orbit to a landing on the Moon's surface. NASA has contracted with both SpaceX to develop its Starship lander and with Blue Origin to develop its Blue Moon lander, as part of Artemis's Human Landing System.

On August 17, 2022, the Artemis I vehicle was rolled out to the launch pad at KSC. After two attempts to launch were scrubbed due to technical issues, the uncrewed Artemis I launched successfully on November 16, 2022.

Orion spent three and a half weeks in space testing the spacecraft's systems and came within approximately 80 miles of the lunar surface at one point. The capsule returned to Earth, splashing down in the Pacific Ocean on December 11, ending a highly successful mission.

As a member of the NAL-JSC Board of Directors, I received an invitation to watch the Artemis I launch from the

Mission Control viewing room at JSC as a guest of Vanessa Wyche, the JSC Director. The launch occurred at 12:47 a.m. Central Time, and it was worth staying up late to watch.

Viewing the Artemis I launch (on small screen at top left of photo) from the Mission Control Center at JSC on November 16, 2022

Astronaut Tom Marshburn, who had recently returned from the ISS, was there with us to talk with us about the mission and answer questions.

Astronaut Tom Marshburn at Artemis I launch in Mission Control at JSC

I was delighted to see some people there whom I had not seen in a long time, including former Flight Director Milt Heflin and former Director of Mission Operations Paul Hill. There were also several friends working at consoles in Mission Control that evening, including Leah Cheshier Mustachio at the Public Affairs Officer (PAO) console, Paul Gramm at the Flight Activity Officer (FAO) console, and Bill Foster at the Ground Control (GC) console. It was a memorable experience—lots of excitement, and the launch was flawless.

* * *

Twenty-five days later, I went to the Teague Auditorium at JSC to watch the Artemis I splashdown. It was a surprisingly emotional event. There were many people in that auditorium who had been working on the Orion Program, either intermittently, like me, or continuously since 2006. That was almost 18 years ago. It's hard to describe how it felt when the first images of that capsule showed up on the big screen and its three main parachutes fully opened as Orion descended slowly into the ocean. The cheering and clapping were louder than I can remember hearing in that auditorium.

Artemis II Crew Selection announcement in April 2023

Five months later, in April 2023, JSC held a ceremony at a hangar at nearby Ellington Field to announce the crew for the Artemis II mission.

The selected astronauts were Commander Reid Wiseman, Pilot Victor Glover, Mission Specialist 1 Christina Koch, and Mission Specialist 2 Jeremy Hansen. It will be the second spaceflight for Wiseman, Glover, and Koch. Hansen, a Canadian astronaut, will be making his first spaceflight.

Herb with Artemis II Commander Reid Wiseman

The selections were kept secret from the public until the day of the announcement. Since these astronauts were being chosen to be the first crew to head to the Moon in more than 50 years, Joe Acaba, Chief of the Astronaut Office, didn't want to simply call or email them with the news. He wanted to gather all three of the NASA astronauts together in the same room without telling them the reason, so that he could surprise them with the news.

The fourth member of the crew, Canadian Jeremy Hansen, would learn the news separately via a phone call from Lisa Campbell, the president of the Canadian Space Agency.

Acaba first chose a day when he knew they would all be at work at JSC. Then, knowing they might become suspicious if they realized they were all being called to the same place at the same time, he created fictional separate meetings for each of them.

Vic Glover was returning from a lunch meeting and texted Acaba, "Hey, boss, I'm going to be a few minutes late."

Christina Koch was at the NBL, several miles from JSC, and she assumed she could attend the meeting remotely. She opened her computer to sign into the meeting but realized there was no meeting link. She sent a text message to Acaba asking, "Hey, can we just meet virtually?" Acaba replied, "Nope." She drove back to JSC as quickly as possible but, she said, "I was late—very late."

Reid Wiseman was at a doctor's office. "Like all good doctor's appointments, this one was going way over," Wiseman said. He informed Acaba that he would miss the meeting, but Acaba asked him to join via videoconference.

When Wiseman joined the meeting remotely, Glover, Koch, and Norm Knight—NASA's Director of Flight Operations, who is Acaba's boss—were all there with Acaba. Wiseman thought, "Oh man, this is not a meeting I should be missing."

After the group was assembled, they were asked rhetorically, "How do you feel about being the crew of Artemis

II?" Afterward, Acaba remarked, "They were all a little late. Luckily, I didn't want to change my mind."

As of today, the Artemis II flight—the first crewed flight of the Artemis Program—is planned for no earlier than September 2025. The crew will fly by the Moon on the planned 10-day mission but will not land on the lunar surface.

Artemis III is planned to be the second crewed Artemis mission and the first crewed lunar landing. The mission is currently scheduled for no earlier than September 2026.

* * *

The pool of astronauts who will potentially walk on the Moon next grew in March 2024 when Astronaut Group 23 graduated from AsCans to astronauts. I attended the graduation ceremony at JSC, where Dr. Harrison 'Jack' Schmitt, who walked on the Moon on Apollo 17, served as the commencement speaker. Ten American astronauts and two UAE astronauts graduated after completing two years of training.

Conference room at JSC in Building 1 where recent interviews were held for Astronaut Candidates (AsCans)

* * *

Finally, I have several friends who hope to become an AsCan/astronaut someday. Some have already applied to at least one astronaut announcement. To those friends, I hope you never give up on your dream.

Whether you're applying to the astronaut program for the first time or the fifteenth time—like Clay Anderson—I wish you the best of luck!

But be prepared for a lot of testing!

Glossary

AA	Associate (or Assistant) Administrator
AFB	Air Force Base
ALHAT	Autonomous Landing and Hazard Avoidance Technology
ALT	Approach and Landing Test
ASE	Association of Space Explorers
ASF	Astronaut Scholarship Foundation
ASPA	American Society for Public Administration
ASTP	Apollo-Soyuz Test Project
ATO	Abort-to-Orbit
AxEMU	Axiom Extravehicular Mobility Unit spacesuit
BBC	British Broadcasting Company
BEAM	Bigelow Expandable Activity Module
CAIB	Columbia Accident Investigation Board
Capcom	Capsule Communicator
CC	Capcom
CCA	Contract Change Authorization
CCAFS	Cape Canaveral Air Force Station
CCB	Contract Change Board
CCCT	Clear Creek Community Theatre
CCHS	Clear Creek High School
CDR	Commander – senior astronaut of a crew
CEV	Crew Exploration Vehicle
CFC	Combined Federal Campaign
CFO	Chief Financial Officer
CLPS	Commercial Lunar Payload Services
CM	Command Module
CMP	Command Module Pilot
CO	Contracting Officer
COTS	Commercial Orbital Transportation Services
CPIT	Change Process Improvement Team
CRS	Commercial Resupply Services
CSM	Command and Service Module
CxP	Constellation Program
DCAA	Defense Contract Audit Agency

DCMA	Defense Contract Management Agency
DDT&E	Design, Development, Test, & Evaluation
DOS	Disk Operating System
EDO	Extended Duration Orbiter
EECOM	Electrical, environmental, & consumables management
EMU	Extravehicular Mobility Unit/spacesuit
ERG	Employee Resource Group
ESA	European Space Agency
ET	External Tank
EVA	Extravehicular activity/spacewalk
FAO	Flight Activities Officer
FAR	Federal Acquisition Regulation
FCOD	Flight Crew Operations Directorate
FDO	Fee Determination Official
FOB	Federal Office Building
FOD	Flight Operations Directorate
FRIDGE	Freezer Refrigerator Incubator Device for Galley and Experimentation
FY	Fiscal Year
GAO	Government Accountability Office
GC	Ground Control
GE	General Electric
G-III	Gulfstream III aircraft
G-V	Gulfstream V aircraft
GSFC	Goddard Space Flight Center
HLS	Human Landing System
INCO	Integrated Communications Officer
ISS	International Space Station
IT	Information Technology
JOFOC	Justification for Other than Full and Open Competition
JPL	Jet Propulsion Lab
JSC	Johnson Space Center
KSC	Kennedy Space Center
KSCVC	Kennedy Space Center Visitor Complex
LaRC	Langley Research Center
LCVG	Liquid Cooling and Ventilation Garment
LLPO	Lunar Lander Project Office
LLRV	Lunar Landing Research Vehicle

LLTV	Lunar Landing Training Vehicle
LM	Lunar Module
LMP	Lunar Module Pilot
LRV	Lunar Roving Vehicle
MAF	Michoud Assembly Facility
MECO	Main Engine Cut-Off
MIT	Massachusetts Institute of Technology
MMU	Manned Maneuvering Unit
MOD	Mission Operations Directorate
MSC	Manned Spacecraft Center (now JSC)
MSFC	Marshall Space Flight Center
NAL-JSC	NASA Alumni League-Johnson Space Center
NBL	Neutral Buoyancy Laboratory
NCMA	National Contract Management Association
NSF	National Science Foundation
OAA	Orbiter Access Arm
OIG	Office of Inspector General
OMS	Orbital Maneuvering System
OPIC	Orion Project Integration Contract
PACE	Professional and Administrative Career Exam
PAO	Public Affairs Office
PNP	Pre-Negotiation Position
PSC	Program Support Contract
RCS	Reaction Control System
RFP	Request for Proposal
RIF	Reduction In Force
RpK	Rocketplane Kistler
S&MA	Safety and Mission Assurance
SAA	Space Act Agreement
SC	Spacecraft
SCA	Shuttle Carrier Aircraft
SCE	Signal Conditioning Electronics
SCH	Space Center Houston
SEB	Source Evaluation Board
SEEC	Space Exploration Educators Conference
SIM	Scientific Instrument Module
SFOC	Space Flight Operations Contract
SLS	Space Launch System
SM	Service Module
SMS-MB	Shuttle Mission Simulator-Motion Base

SPT	Science Pilot
SRB	Solid Rocket Booster
SSME	Space Shuttle Main Engine
STEM	Science, Technology, Engineering, and Math
STG	Space Task Group
STS	Space Transportation System
SVMF	Space Vehicle Mockup Facility
TFNG	Thirty-Five New Guys
TRS	Teleoperator Retrieval System
TWX	TeletypeWriter eXchange
USA	United Space Alliance
USSR	Union of Soviet Socialist Republics
UT	The University of Texas
VFW	Veterans of Foreign Wars
WELL	Women Excelling in Life and Leadership
WETF	Weightless Environment Training Facility
WP	Work Package
WSTF	White Sands Test Facility
xEMU	Exploration Extravehicular Mobility Unit

Acknowledgments

I've been inspired in this book-writing adventure by several friends who have authored books about NASA. One was David Chudwin, who published his book, *I was a Teenage Space Reporter*, several years ago. His early life story is similar to mine in that we were both teenagers at the time of the Apollo 11 lunar landing mission—he was 19 and I was 17—and we were members of the press corps covering that mission. He was at the Kennedy Space Center (KSC) in Florida and I was at the Manned Spacecraft Center (MSC) in Houston. David went to Medical School and became a doctor specializing in allergy/immunology. He recently published his second book, *The Magical Decade: A personal memoir and popular history of 1965-75*.

Two other friends have also recently written books about their personal experiences with NASA, providing further inspiration. Jean Wright recently published her book titled *Sew Sister: The Untold Story of Jean Wright and NASA Seamstresses*.

A friend in the U.K., Sue Nelson, published her book, *Wally Funk's Race for Space: The Extraordinary Story of a Female Aviation Pioneer*, in 2018. I was honored that Sue mentioned my work at NASA and the story of Mom sewing the Skylab parasol in her book.

Several other friends have authored or co-authored books about NASA, as well.

Bruce McCandless III who, like me, grew up in the community around JSC, has published several books, including

Wonders All Around: The Incredible True Story of Astronaut Bruce McCandless II and the First Untethered Flight in Space, about his father.

Francis French has at least six books to his credit, including *Falling to Earth: An Apollo 15 Astronaut's Journey to the Moon*, which he co-authored with Apollo 15 astronaut Al Worden.

Jonathan Ward has at least four books to his credit, including *Bringing Columbia Home*, which he co-authored with former Shuttle Launch Director Mike Leinbach.

Astronaut Rhea Seddon, who self-published her book, *Go for Orbit*, a few years ago, gave me two pieces of useful advice. I had a chance to talk with her about her book-writing experience, and she told me, "Don't be afraid to self-publish and to find a good editor."

I also want to thank the hundreds of NASA friends and co-workers I've known over my career who have supported, mentored, and encouraged me along the way. What a journey it has been!

About the Author

Herb Baker grew up just a few miles from the Manned Spacecraft Center (MSC), which opened when he was 11 years old. By that time, the first three groups of astronauts had been selected, and they had moved their families into the rapidly growing community near Houston.

He was friends and classmates with many children of astronauts and other NASA employees through junior high and high school. His first job at NASA was as a member of the news media at the age of 17, covering the Apollo 11 mission on-site at MSC while working alternately for the ABC, NBC, and Metromedia networks. He also worked on-site with those networks covering Apollo 12, Apollo 13, Apollo 15, and two Skylab missions.

His mother, Alyene Baker, played a role in saving the Skylab mission as the seamstress who sewed the parasol that replaced the space station's missing micrometeoroid heat shield.

Herb began his professional career at NASA in 1975 in the procurement office at Johnson Space Center. He worked at JSC for a total of 31 years, at NASA Headquarters for 10 years, and at KSC for nine months on a special assignment.

During that period, he supported the Space Shuttle Program, the Space Station Program, and the Constellation Program (including Orion). He also supported Flight Operations (including the Astronaut Office), Safety and Mission Assurance, Human Health & Performance, and Engineering, among several other organizations.

With his background and knowledge of the space program, he was often asked to give guided tours of the Mission Control rooms, the Neutral Buoyancy Lab, the Space Vehicle Mockup Facility, Rocket Park, and other areas at JSC.

He was awarded the NASA Exceptional Service Medal in 2010 and retired in 2017 after 42 years of service. Since retiring, he has spent most of his time volunteering for nonprofit organizations supporting STEM education, including the NASA Alumni League-JSC (where he serves as an officer on the board of directors), the Astronaut Scholarship Foundation, Space Center Houston, and the Remembering *Columbia* Museum in Hemphill, TX.

He is also a frequent speaker to students and other organizations, a frequent guest on podcasts, and participates in many other interviews and presentations about human space exploration.

His other interests include acting in community theater (having appeared on stage in more than 20 shows), playing the trombone as a member of the Longhorn Alumni Band, and writing.

Bibliography

Allen, Joseph P., "NASA Johnson Space Center Oral History Project," NASA. *Johnson Space Center - NASA*. https://historycollection.jsc.nasa.gov/JSCHistoryPortal/history/oral_histories/AllenJP/ allenjp.htm

Carr, Gerald P., "NASA Johnson Space Center Oral History Project," NASA. *Johnson Space Center - NASA*. https://historycollection.jsc.nasa.gov/JSCHistoryPortal/history/oral_histories/CarrGP/CarrGP_10-25-00.htm

Cassutt, Michael. (2018). *The Astronaut Maker: How One Mysterious Engineer Ran Human Spaceflight for a Generation* (1st ed.). Chicago Review Press Incorporated.

Columbia Accident Investigation Board: Report Volume I. (2003). Columbia Accident Investigation Board. https://sma.nasa.gov/SignificantIncidents/assets/columbia-accident-investigation-board-report-volume-1.pdf

Dethloff, Henry C. (1994). *Suddenly, Tomorrow Came: A History of the Johnson Space Center*. http://hdl.handle.net/2060/19940020111

Ezell, Edward Clinton & Ezell, Linda Neuman. (1977). *The Partnership: A History of the Apollo-Soyuz Test Project*. National Aeronautics and Space Administration. https://www.hq.nasa.gov/ pao/History/SP-4209/toc.htm

Fabian, John M. "NASA Johnson Space Center Oral History Project," NASA. *Johnson Space Center - NASA*.

https://historycollection.jsc.nasa.gov/JSCHistoryPortal/histo
ry/oral_histories/FabianJM/ fabianjm.htm

Fendell, Edward I., "NASA Johnson Space Center Oral
History Project," NASA. *Johnson Space Center - NASA.*
https://historycollection.jsc.nasa.gov/JSCHistoryPortal/histo
ry/oral_histories/FendellEI/fendellei.htm

Hadfield, Chris. (2013). *An astronaut's guide to life on Earth: What
going to space taught me about ingenuity, determination, and being
prepared for anything.* https://openlibrary.org/books/
OL26263479M/An_Astronaut's_Guide_to_Life_on_Earth

Hansen, Chris (2019). *ISS EVA 23 Lessons Learned: Date of
Mishap: July 16, 2013.* NASA Johnson Space Center.
https://ntrs.nasa.gov/api/citations/20230002544/downloads
/EVA23_Lessons_Learned_BASE(2a).pdf

Hansen, James R. (2018). *First Man: The Life of Neil A.
Armstrong* (Reissue). Simon & Schuster.

Heinz, Frank. (2021, February 4). Spacecraft named after
NASA mathematician Katherine Johnson heading to
ISS. *NBC4 Washington.* https://www.nbcwashington.com/
news/national-international/spacecraft-headed-to-iss-named-
after-legendary-nasa-mathematician-katherine-
johnson/2562431/

Information Summaries: Space Station (PMS-008). (1986). National
Aeronautics and Space Administration.
https://files.eric.ed.gov/fulltext/ED326378.pdf

NASA. *Johnson Space Center - NASA.*
https://nasa.gov/johnson

NASA Spaceflight webpage. (2005, August 31). NASASpaceflight.com. https://www.nasaspaceflight.com/ 2005/08/nasa-chief-outlines-exploration-vision/

Nicogossian, Arnauld E., MD (Ed.). (1977). *The Apollo-Soyuz Test Project: Medical Report* (NASA SP-411). National Aeronautics and Space Administration. https://ntrs.nasa.gov/citations/ 19770023791

O'Hara, Dolores "Dee" B., "NASA Johnson Space Center Oral History Project," NASA. *Johnson Space Center - NASA.* https://historycollection.jsc.nasa.gov/JSCHistoryPortal/histo ry/oral_histories/ OHaraDB/oharadb.htm

Performance Summary, Space Shuttle Program: STS-1 Flight (STS 81-0378). (1981). Rockwell International.

Report of the Presidential Commission on the Space Shuttle Challenger Accident. (1986). In *https://ntrs.nasa.gov /citations/19860015255.* Presidential Commission on the Space Shuttle Challenger Accident. https://ntrs.nasa.gov/ api/citations/19860015255/downloads/ 19860015255.pdf

Schweickart, Russell L., "NASA Johnson Space Center Oral History Project," NASA. *Johnson Space Center - NASA.* https://historycollection.jsc.nasa.gov/ JSCHistoryPortal/ history/oral_histories /SchweickartRL/schweickartrl.htm

Seddon, Rhea. (2015) *Go For Orbit: One of America's First Women Astronauts Finds Her Space.* Your Space Press. https://astronautrheaseddon.com/product/go-for-orbit/

Shaw, Brewster H. "NASA Johnson Space Center Oral History Project," NASA. *Johnson Space Center - NASA.* https://historycollection.jsc.nasa.gov/JSCHistoryPortal/histo ry/oral_histories/ ShawBH/shawbh.htm

Shepard, Jr., Alan B., "NASA Johnson Space Center Oral History Project," NASA. *Johnson Space Center - NASA*. https://historycollection.jsc.nasa.gov/JSCHistoryPortal/histo ry/oral_histories/ShepardAB/ShepardAB_2-20-98.htm

Swanson, Glen E. (Ed.). (1999). *Before This Decade is Out: Personal Reflections on the Apollo Program* (NASA SP-4223). NASA. https://ntrs.nasa.gov/api/citations/ 20000027506/ downloads/ 20000027506.pdf

Printed in Great Britain
by Amazon

57539134R00199